THE YOUNG BRONTËS

The Young Brontës

Charlotte and Emily, Branwell and Anne

BY MARY LOUISE JARDEN

With illustrations by Helen Sewell

NEW YORK : THE VIKING PRESS

FIRST PUBLISHED OCTOBER 1938

SECOND PRINTING OCTOBER 1940

THIRD PRINTING MARCH 1944

FOURTH PRINTING FEBRUARY 1946

FIFTH PRINTING FEBRUARY 1949

SIXTH PRINTING MAY 1953

SEVENTH PRINTING SEPTEMBER 1958

EIGHTH PRINTING OCTOBER 1961

NINTH PRINTING NOVEMBER 1963

The author makes acknowledgment as follows: to Mrs. H. H. Bonnell, whose kind introductions to Brontë lovers unlocked the "Brontë country" to the author; and to Mr. and Mrs. Edward Loring Thomas, whose tireless encouragement and criticism made this book possible.

CONTENTS

ILLUSTRATIONS

Chapter One

THE GENII COME INTO
THEIR OWN

O VER the Moor the brown of autumn flowed like a golden film in the red stretches of sunset. The stillness of early evening was broken only by the occasional sharp bleat of a sheep as, frightened by a swooping hawk, it leaped off over the knotted grass hummocks. A flock of swallows would go noisily overhead, in eager hurry to get away from the rigorous winter in this part of northern England.

From farm yards in the villages round about came the squawking of hens, battling over the few fragments of their evening meal, or the more contented gruntings of a litter of pigs.

Factories whose chimneys had belched smoke all day long were now empty and dark, along the road from Keighley to Haworth.

But there was something moving along that road, towards Haworth, something which set the hens squawking anew.

It was a covered cart, creaking along on rusty wheels, the sort of vehicle that was used daily to carry woolen or cotton goods from the near-by factories to the larger cities of Manchester and Leeds.

But this cart was not carrying wool or cotton. Against the darkening sky appeared the silhouettes of two men. One was a shaggy-haired driver, and the other a big man with a hat like a stove pipe, his long black coat tails swaying behind him, hanging from the high seat. His chin was muffled in a large silk, scarf-like cravat.

Suddenly his head turned. His voice rang out clearly over the squeak and clatter of the cart wheels upon the cobble stones.

"Is all well with you, children?"

On the floor, at his back, two gray blankets stirred, and heaved. Out popped two small and weary faces surmounted by black bombazine bonnets, like overturned coal scuttles, sadly askew.

They were little girls. In concert they answered him.

"Yes, Papa! Thank you, Papa!"

The big man turned his back once more upon them. He had to lean forward in order to keep his balance, as they jolted along the highway.

But the girls rolled back and forth inside their blankets like two small nuts in a very large bowl. And suddenly, bump! They went into each other!

"Ouch! My nose!" Charlotte gasped.

"My chin!" cried Emily.

They sat up. They threw back the thick folds of blanket and looked at each other. They stood up, to look over the edge of the jerking cart.

"Good gracious!" Charlotte's eyes grew big. "Only see how far we have come. We are already at Keighley."

"We are nearly home!" said Emily joyously.

"We are further every minute," Charlotte sighed, "from the girls and the good time at school."

Charlotte sank back onto the floor of the cart, pulling the gray blanket, once more, to her chin. But Emily stood still,

swaying and jolting with the cart, and heard in the squeaking
wheels the same chant, over and over again: "To the Moor!
. . . To the Moor! . . . Home to the Moor!"

Two long months she had been away, two months with
Charlotte at Cowan Bridge School. There had been no wide
sweeping hills there, but only thickly wooded valleys all about
the school building. She had had to live in damp, cold cot-
tages, and to sleep in a long room among girls all older and
bigger than herself. Even when she had managed to run away
from them and from the narrow school rooms and make her
escape to the woods outside, the sight of the dismal, leaning
willow trees had only made her cry and cry, until her throat
ached, for the stiff thorn tree in the garden at home and the
wide freedom of the Moor beyond.

Then, just as it had seemed that she could bear no more,
news had arrived from home.

Times were bad in Haworth. Papa could not collect the
church fees from his congregation. He could not afford to
pay for another term at school for Emily and Charlotte. He
was coming at once to fetch them home. Emily had wanted
to cry for joy; but Charlotte had cried miserably:

"I don't care if it is disagreeable here in the winter and
if we do get chilblains on our feet. It is a school and we are
learning history and geography and grammar. And I was just
beginning the study of arithmetic. But now it is no use, for
I shall be just an ignorant nobody!"

Emily, rolling and jolting nearly on top of her older sister,
felt herself so brimful of happiness that it seemed it must
surely overflow to Charlotte. She fumbled in her mind to
speak the words which were singing through her, but the

very deepness of her joy seemed to hold her silent. Only the climbing wheels of the old cart squeaked over and over again: "To the Moor! Home to the Moor!"

"Emily! Please! Stop humming! I can't stand it."

Charlotte struggled forward. She threw back the blanket and stretched both arms out to relieve them of their cramped position.

"Have you thought," she demanded, "about how awful it will be to live at home without Maria or Elizabeth, and with only Aunt to care for us?"

Emily looked about, startled, into Charlotte's brown, miserable eyes.

She wrinkled her forehead to remember the faces of her two sisters who had died last spring, even older than Charlotte; but already their memory was very shadowy, and merged somehow with the sweet-smelling thought of snowdrops and early crocuses pushing through the earth in the garden. She said:

"There will be Branwell, though he is only a boy. And there is always little Anne. And Aunt cannot be so very different from Mother, since she was her own sister."

But Charlotte murmured reproachfully:

"You cannot remember Mother. She was lovely and pale, and not one bit like Aunt."

Up and on jerked the cart, over the rough cobbles. Once more Emily and Charlotte were thrown against each other as they made a sudden right turn, rumbling over a bridge.

"It is the bridge below Haworth, over our river, our little flowing beck," Emily nearly shouted.

"There," she pointed, "is the Fleece Inn! And there is the

house of Will Eccles. See! The windows are lighted in the top room. He must be working late at his loom."

Up and up they climbed on the twisting road. Past Mrs. Rushforth's spice shop. Emily could almost look in through the round window and see the cakes and spices laid out on the shelves. Beyond Mrs. Rushforth's was the shop of Tom Pickels, the butcher, whose cellar was hung with rows and rows of whole muttons and whole pigs, ready dressed.

"There is the village school, and the Black Bull Inn."

"And the church, and the graveyard!" breathed Charlotte.

It was Emily who caught first sight of the end of their journey.

"There it is. There is our own house. It is lit up to welcome us home."

It was a square brown house; sturdy stone, even to the thick slabs of blue stone upon its roof. And beyond it, still blue, rose the hills of the Moor. They knew that they were home at last, to stay.

Papa was giving an order to the driver.

"Stop at the front gate, John Brown. You may bring in the boxes when you have finished your duties as sexton in the church. Be sure that it is well cleaned for the morrow's service."

John Brown reined in the horse with a terrific jerk. Papa climbed stiffly over the hub of the big wheel to the ground. He groaned, stretching his legs for the first time in nine hours.

Charlotte and Emily scrambled out of their blankets to clamber across the driver's seat. John Brown lifted them down to Papa, each in turn.

The minute that Charlotte was upon her feet she put up her hands to her bonnet to set it straight. Quickly she turned to give a touch to Emily's.

"Your hair is all in wisps over your ears. There, that is more orderly. Does mine appear proper?"

Emily nodded, but her eyes were on the first blinking stars above the church tower and the blue deep round of the afterglow across the hills.

Charlotte touched her shoulder.

"Come along in. See, the door is open. And there are Aunt and Branwell and Anne."

The open doorway shed a beam of light over the stone steps. The girls ran through the gate and up the path after Papa.

Suddenly, out from the front door shot the dark form of a boy. He rushed down the steps toward them. He was waving both hands above his head, shouting:

"Good for you. You're here at last!"

A little girl was following after him, as fast as her small legs would carry her. Her voice echoed her brother's words.

"You're here at last."

Branwell seized Charlotte by both shoulders and spun her completely around in his jubilant welcome.

"I say, it is good to have you back, Charlotte. You've no idea how dull it is around here without you. From now on things will begin to hum again!"

Anne was running from one to the other of her sisters, lifting big blue eyes to theirs. She clung to Emily to whisper:

"Will you take care of me? I'm the smallest. And I'm frightened when there is no one to take care of me."

Emily knelt suddenly on the step, with her arm around Anne and Anne's small, fair head on her shoulder.

They came, all four together, into the hallway of the parsonage.

Two candles, placed upon the table, flickered to give the room light. They gleamed and shone on the rustling black silk dress and wide, stiff, lace collar of a tall and exceedingly thin woman. It was Aunt.

Her monstrous, snowy-white cap quivered in the breeze blowing from the open door. Beneath it was a stiff fringe of auburn curls. Her eyes were gray and distant.

"Good evening, children."

Charlotte and Emily let go of Branwell and Anne, to jerk bobbing curtsies.

"Good evening, Aunt."

"Did you stand your journey well?"

"Very well, thank you, Aunt," Charlotte answered, with another curtsy.

"Ah, well, you had better remove your bonnets and cloaks, and wash your faces. Tabby is waiting tea for you."

"Tabby?"

Emily and Charlotte turned, inquiringly, toward their brother and sister.

"Is Tabby a new servant?" asked Charlotte.

Branwell nodded. His blue eyes and the red mop of his hair twinkled like other flames in the candle light.

"Yes, and she's quite all right, though she can be hard to move as the Moor itself once she makes up her mind to a thing."

The girls ran up a long flight of stone steps, from the hallway to the second floor. Directly at the top of the stairs was the doorway of their own room.

Inside was the big four-poster bed where they were to sleep together. Its feather mattress rose and fell in soft humps and billows, indistinct in the faint light.

They had to feel their way to avoid bumping into the high dresser. They could hardly see into their tiny mirror by the dim light, but neither would have suggested having a candle. It would have been needless extravagance, and vanity as well, to have a light made to dress by.

They stopped only long enough to take off their bonnets and warm heavy cloaks and coat-like pelisses, and to straighten out the white pleated collars of their dresses. Then they hurried down again, out through the kitchen to wash their hands and faces at the pump.

As they came into the kitchen the good smell of oat-cakes rose to them. Before the glowing fire, half hiding it from their view, was a huge woman. She was bending over, her back toward them. Curiously the girls eyed the square shoulders and the wide, thick-set body of the new servant.

A moment later they were out in the yard splashing at the pump. Emily said:

"I am hungry enough to eat all those oat-cakes by myself." Charlotte blinked the water from her eyes, amazed.

"You hungry? But you are never hungry. Why, at school I've seen you take a whipping rather than have your tea. That is why you are so thin!"

Emily flung up her head to the twinkling stars above, and answered:

"This is not school. It is home, and I am going to get fat."

They dried their hands on a coarse linen towel, and hurried back through the kitchen.

Now Tabby stood upright. She had a huge tea kettle in one hand, and in the other a plate of thin-sliced, buttered bread. Her face, beneath the line of her dull blond hair, was dark and weathered like the bark of the thorn tree in the garden outside. She made no motion of greeting, but turned away from them to go into the dining room. Emily said:

"I think I am going to like Tabby."

Charlotte demanded:

"How do you know? I do not think she is very polite, if you ask my opinion."

"I like to look at her. She seems permanent, like the Moor."

"Well," said Charlotte. "That is odd. Branwell said the very same thing of her. Only he called it 'hard to move.' "

During tea Papa ate enormously and talked across the dining-room table to Aunt. He told her:

"There was some indignation at Cowan Bridge that I should have removed my two daughters before the end of the term. However, I am satisfied, my dear Miss Branwell, that their place is at home assisting you with the cares of the household." He wiped his mouth with the back of his hand, adding: "Moreover, as it happened, I had other business in that neighborhood today. It might not have suited my convenience so well, to bring them at another time."

The good oat-cakes and tea were doing queer things to Charlotte. She said:

"I never thought I could eat so much, but it all tastes so good. And the bread is not soggy, as it was at school."

"At school," said Emily, "the tea was always cold. And they did not give us butter."

"No butter!" Branwell exclaimed. "But you cannot eat bread without butter."

"We did, or else went without."

At Emily's elbow a voice broke suddenly in on them, a harsh, ringing voice.

"Cold tea! Bad bread sinna butter! Small wonder tha'rt peaky. It were na more nor time we had ye home, poor childer!"

It was Tabby. Abruptly she turned and stalked away back to the kitchen. Aunt gasped.

"The impudence of the servant class in these parts! I declare, it is quite unbelievable."

Her hand fumbled suddenly at her waist. She was muttering half to herself.

"Where is my snuffbox? I must have my snuffbox. I am exceedingly upset."

With a spasmodic jerk she brought out a tiny brown box. It hung like a huge locket from a thin gold chain about her neck. Aunt snapped open the lid. She shook out a good pinch of the brown sawdusty particles upon the crotch of her thumb. Delicately she applied it first to one, then to the other arching nostril. For a moment she inhaled deeply. There was a pause.

Then suddenly she sneezed. Once. Twice. Every ribbon of her cap vibrated. The fringe of auburn curls beneath it was pushed awry, to reveal her smooth forehead.

Calmly Aunt tucked the snuffbox away and pinned the false "front" of auburn curls back into place. By the time that

Tabby had returned, she was continuing serenely with her dinner.

After tea Aunt ordered all the children off to bed at once. But Branwell lingered in the doorway of the girls' room.

"That last letter you wrote me from school, Charlotte, was fine. About how you played the battle of Waterloo, and you were the Duke of Wellington. Do you recall it?"

"Yes. I recall it!"

"It sounded like such a splendid game. Why could we not play it here?" A step sounded suddenly on the stairs. Branwell scurried off to the big room which he shared with Papa.

It was Aunt. In her hand was a candle. It made sharp lines from her long nose to her eyes. Her mouth, speaking, moved absurdly up and down:

"Tabby is an arrogant servant, but she tells the truth. It is Providence that you are both removed from that school whose unhealthy climate caused the deaths of your two older sisters. Moreover"—she hesitated, and looked down to pinch the candle wick between her fingers—"moreover, it will be pleasant to have you back. This parsonage has been lonely without you."

Aunt pattered on down the hall. They heard the door of her room shut firmly.

Emily undressed close to the window, so that she could look down upon the twinkling lights of Haworth below. They spread like the faint reflections of the glittering points of stars. As far as her eyes could see, they came on and shone and then seemed to vanish once more into the hills and into the sky above. She said:

"They are going to sleep, down in the Bottom."

But the hills would be there tomorrow, and the next day, and forever. She turned and crept into the humpy feather bed beside Charlotte.

"Emily, I have decided something."

"What have you decided?"

Emily yawned in the great peace of sleepiness. Charlotte was quiet for a moment, then she burst out:

"Oh, Emily, is not Anne a darling? We must take great care of her. And I must tell Branwell some more about our plays. I should not be surprised if he were quite as good at 'making out' plays and stories as the girls at school."

"Is that what you have decided?"

"No, not entirely." Charlotte hesitated. Then slowly she spoke: "I have been thinking about Mother and Maria and Elizabeth, all gone to heaven, and leaving me here with the rest of you to care for. And I wonder if they may not think, perhaps, that I do not need an education so much as Branwell and little Anne need to be looked after. I have decided that it is a good thing, after all, that Papa came to fetch us home from school."

Chapter Two

THE GENII DISCOVER
THEIR KINGDOM

" **A** ND Aladdin took the wonderful lamp and rubbed it. Suddenly there was a great rumbling under the earth, and a great cloud of smoke, and a voice spoke out of the smoke: 'I am one of the most powerful Genii in the world. What would you have me do for you?' "

The *Arabian Nights* lay closed on Charlotte's lap. Her eyes were on the round of the blue sky. She leaned back comfortably against a sunny rock, telling to Branwell and Emily and Anne from memory the story of Aladdin.

It was an early June afternoon of the year 1826. Yellow gorse was budding and ferny bracken was uncurling and spreading to leafy bright patches along the Moor.

The children were in their favorite place on the Moor at the edge of a long, flowing stream called Sladen Beck, and in the shelter of a high brown rock.

Sladen Beck started up among the highest hills and wound down gradually among the rocks until, rushing past their shelter, it was almost a waterfall. Below, it fell to a larger beck called the River Aire.

In places along Sladen Beck the rocks were so hollowed out by the force of the water as to form sheltered pools.

By one such pool Emily and Anne lay on their stomachs, chins on their hands, watching for wee brown tadpoles swimming about in the clear water.

Branwell lay out flat on his back on the heather, listening to make sure Charlotte would leave out no part of the story.

"And so," she concluded, "Aladdin and the beautiful princess lived happily ever after, thanks to all the Genii."

For a moment none of the children spoke. The singing wind brought new earth-smells spicy with heather, the sounds of birds high in the blue above them, and deep content not easily ruffled into thought.

"What are Genii?" It was Anne who asked.

"Genii," Charlotte answered, "are the most powerful beings in the world."

"If I," said Emily, "were one of the Genii, I would live all summer long on top of the Moor. And when winter came I would rush down the hills and ride through the Bottom in howling blizzards."

"If I were one of the Genii," Branwell declared, "I would have a sword and an army of my own, and a fine ship to go adventuring in."

"No!" Charlotte shook her head. "Genii do not go adventuring themselves. They bring adventures to brave and deserving human beings like . . . like . . ."

"The Duke of Wellington!" said Branwell.

Anne said:

"They sound very mysterious, and I am afraid of mysterious things."

"True Genii," Charlotte declared, "are afraid of nothing."

Anne raised awed, blue eyes to her sister's.

"Not even of Papa? When he is preaching about hell?"

"Not even that."

"I know of an adventure we might have," Branwell put in,

"which is worthy of the Genii. What do you say to our bearding the ogre, Tabby, in her den? I smelt raisin cakes upon the bake stone as we came out."

"Raisin cakes!" Charlotte jumped up, letting the *Arabian Nights* slide to the ground. "Why did you not speak of them before? I am famished."

Down they ran along the footpath through the pink heather buds, treading down the golden cups and daisies in their hungry advance. One after another they slid down the bank to the little green lane which led back to the parsonage.

They found Tabby by the pump, with a tall washtub before her. Her elbows were deep in suds and the family wash. She was wringing out Papa's long white silk cravat, which he wore wound round and round his neck.

Branwell came up behind her on his tip-toes.

"Boo! I'm one of the Genii!"

He sprang away as Tabby, for all her weight, suddenly swung on him. Her eyebrows were white flecked and threatening.

"I know ye, Branwell. Begone, every one o' ye. Ill childer!"

"We want some raisin cakes," said Charlotte.

"Ye can make t' wait till tea time."

"But we are hungry now."

"We are starving!" said Branwell. "We are so weak that we can scarcely walk."

"Ha' done with such talk, ye madlin'." Tabby flung down two more soapy towels on the pile in the basket, muttering something about "disturbing a body at her work"; then, abruptly she turned and started off for the kitchen. She climbed heavily onto the high step and disappeared within.

"Is she angry with us?" Anne asked anxiously. But Emily said:

"She has gone to get us something to eat."

Sure enough, within a minute Tabby was back again with four mugs brimful of milk and a pile of brown raisin cakes.

They drank thirstily from the big mugs. All of them were plain white china except Emily's, which had her name printed in silver upon it. Hers had been given to her as a christening mug when she was a baby.

Tabby was back at the washtub, rubbing hard to make up for time lost.

Emily told her:

"You should smell it, up on the Moor today. It is like magic."

"Magic!" Tabby grunted. "Aye, best guard thyself o' magic on th' Moor. Or th' witch o' th' Moor'll find thee, certain!"

"The witch of the Moor!"

Emily demanded:

"What is the witch of the Moor?"

"I know," said Branwell. "John Brown told me. He says that it is the ghost of a beautiful woman who lived far off by herself, upon the Moor."

Tabby straightened. Aunt's cap splashed back into the soapy suds.

"Ghosts! Na, this one is no dead spirit. John Brown would ne'er know. Wi' his grave diggin' and th' drink at th' Black Bull. Th' witch o' th' Moor is a live demon. And strange things happen where she is about."

She went once more to the swirling suds. She rubbed and dipped and squeezed the drops of water from pantalets and petticoats and sheets in the mighty grip of her fingers. A fine spray touched the children sitting on the grass as Aunt's cap was given a final twist and sent flying after the rest of the clean clothes into the basket.

Charlotte asked:

"Does the witch of the Moor have long flowing hair? And does she moan dismally?"

"Na, dinna plague me more," Tabby grumbled. "There's ower much work lyin' at th' wall. Begone t' your play."

Branwell bent close to the tub, demanding:

"Tell us, first, what are her eyes like? And what would happen to us if we should meet her?"

But Tabby was worn beyond patience at last.

"Begone! Begone, ye madlin'. Ye'll be muckin' th' wash. Begone, I tell ye!"

She had seized the washboard in her brawny arms. Black and furious, she made at them, recklessly wasting good suds on the grass. They took to their heels and fled.

That night Papa returned late from a journey to Leeds. Charlotte, lying in bed, heard the squeak of cart wheels on the street and the clap of horse's hoofs and John Brown's familiar drawl.

"Good even, Mr. Brontë." Papa's sonorous rumble answered:

"The Lord be with you, John Brown."

Charlotte turned over, and slept. She was startled awake by a sudden rattling at the door and Branwell's voice, calling:

"Emily! Charlotte! See what Papa brought home with him last night from Leeds."

By the time Charlotte had brushed the sleep from her eyes Emily was out of bed, with her long tail of dark hair swinging down her back.

Branwell did not wait for them to open the door. Like a whirlwind he came into the room. He was in his long white night-shirt and rattled a long box high above his head.

The girls knelt barefooted in their night-gowns, on the carpetless floor. Breathlessly they watched as Branwell lifted the lid of the box.

There, side by side in the full red and white regalia of the Duke of Wellington's crack militia, were twelve brightly painted wooden soldiers, each with a sword ready in his hand.

"There, how's that for a royal army!" he demanded.

Charlotte swooped down upon the largest and handsomest of the troop.

"This is the Duke of Wellington!" She waved it high, repeating: "This shall be the Duke."

Emily picked out another soldier.

"I want this one. He has not such a silly grin as the others."

Branwell ran off to get dressed, leaving the box still open on the floor. Hastily the girls pulled on their clothes as Charlotte planned busily what they should do with the toys.

"We will call them the Twelve Adventurers, and the Duke of Wellington shall lead them." She went on: "Good gracious, Emily, why ever did you pick out that gloomy one for yours? He should be called 'Gravey' to match his sour looks."

Anne, who slept in Aunt's room, was down and waiting for them when they made their appearance in the hallway. Branwell was not long in following.

With shining eyes Anne picked one for her own, a grand soldier with a hat like a huge white muff perched on top of his head and gold braid fastened beneath his chin. Branwell called the hat a "shako." Charlotte told her:

"Your soldier has a round face like yours. We will call him 'Waiting Boy,' and he can keep the Duke's boots clean. But, Branwell, you've not chosen your own."

Branwell picked out one with a very rotund stomach, as much shorter than the others as Charlotte's was taller.

"Mine," he said, "is Napoleon. I shall call him Bonaparte for short."

Emily ran suddenly to throw open the front door. Like a warm living creature the air rushing up the Moor poured in upon them, driving out the dampness of the cold hallway, and bringing smells of every growing thing from the sunlit garden.

"And now"—Charlotte turned firmly about—"we must go in to breakfast with Papa. He will be angry if we have kept him waiting."

Charlotte opened the door into Papa's study. Behind her trooped the others.

All they could see of Papa was the wide-spread pages of the *Manchester Guardian,* gripped by two large red-knuckled hands and topped by a brown forehead with a thin strand of gray hair rising straight up on it, just like Branwell's red tuft.

On the table was spread breakfast: four steaming bowls of porridge and a great pitcher of milk laid on a clean white cloth. Papa's bowl was gray and nearly twice as large as the others.

"Good morning, Papa!" said Charlotte to the *Manchester*

Guardian. The rest took their places in silence about him and unfolded their big linen napkins expectantly.

The porridge smelled particularly good and spicy this morning. Emily's nose quivered, sniffing at it like a little animal. Anne peered anxiously into her bowl to see that it was quite as full as the others. Branwell, who was always ready to eat, seized hold of his spoon and would have started immediately had not Charlotte kicked him beneath the table and whispered:

"Wait until Papa says the blessing. We must none of us do anything that will make us be kept in today."

Branwell dropped his spoon back on the table with a horrible clatter. There was not even a quiver of the *Manchester Guardian.*

The high cased clock in the hall ticked on and on as Papa read. Emily, by screwing around, could just catch a glimpse of the edge of the page he was reading. She peered as far as she dared. Sinking back in her seat, she held up two significant fingers.

Branwell nearly groaned aloud. Papa on page two! And there were four pages in all! With the porridge growing cold.

Charlotte knew that all the parliamentary speeches were on page two. She tried to frown Branwell down when he put his fingers to his ear and waved the other arm in imitation of an elephant. She wondered curiously what Papa could be reading that absorbed him so unusually long. He was generally content with one or two columns before breakfast. There must be some desperately exciting news. Charlotte tingled to the thought.

Suddenly down came the *Manchester Guardian* and two

fists upon the table. The voice of the Reverend Patrick Branwell Brontë spoke forth loudly and violently across the porridge bowls.

"How much longer shall we endure the rule of that lily-
livered wretch who calls himself Prime Minister of England!
That abominable weakling, Lord Liverpool!"

Emily and Anne nearly jumped out of their chairs. Charlotte cleared her throat, feeling that it would be impolite not
to answer Papa, since he had asked a question.

"Why," she floundered. "That is—I suppose—" But Papa swept her to silence with a wave of his hand.

"Panic! That is what we have. That is the pass to which Lord Liverpool's administration has brought us, panic and ruin for thousands of manufacturers. High taxes!"

Papa's white silk cravat billowed and bulged about his neck as he flung out both arms suddenly. It was a well-known gesture in the pulpit at the Haworth church, as was also the one which followed it. He drew back one arm and with a returning swoop shook an all-inclusive finger at the group.

"What we need is a strong man at the helm. We need the fire which led England to victory at the battle of Waterloo. We need, in short, a statesman like the Duke of Wellington."

"The Duke of Wellington!" Charlotte felt as if an electric spark had passed up her spine. "Has he made a speech? Is it in the *Manchester Guardian?* Was he wearing the royal crimson decoration across his bosom?"

Slowly Papa's neck turned toward her. He glared unseeingly at the top of her head for the space of three seconds before he answered:

"The Duke of Wellington is at present, as Minister of Foreign Affairs, examining into the state of Russia. He is absent from the country at this time. But he will return. He will return to save England!"

Then suddenly, and before any of them had quite dared hope for it, Papa raised both hands for a prayer of grace:

"Now, O Lord, we pray Thee to bless this food which we shall feed to our miserable bodies . . ."

In another minute the children fell to eating with most grateful appetites. Even Papa dipped into his porridge bowl and poured out milk with a generous hand. The clatter of pewter spoons against the home-baked crockery rose in a rhythmic note.

Charlotte's eyes wandered again to the crumpled pages of the *Manchester Guardian*. She wondered if it would be there when they came back from the Moor, with all the account about Parliament, long words and italics and, best of all, the tiny section which was devoted to the description of the clothing of the lords of Parliament.

"I should like," said Emily, "some sugar."

Papa reached a long and energetic arm across the table to pass it to her. Unlike Aunt, Papa was not concerned with such small matters as a "please," or a "thank you."

When he saw that Papa was not looking, Branwell made a gesture of holding his nose as his lips formed the word: Liv—er—pool. And he winked violently at Charlotte. Charlotte pretended, disapprovingly, that she did not see him.

Morning lessons were got through without mishap to either Branwell or the girls. After they had had their mutton, Branwell ran upstairs to get the precious box which contained their new toys, the Twelve Adventurers.

With one accord they started for Sladen Beck. Out along the footpath they ran, climbing once more up the bank from the little green lane and striding up the Moor with the wind in their faces and the pale ling heather at their feet.

"I wonder," said Charlotte, "if there could be any truth in what Tabby says about the witch of the Moor."

"Pooh! It is all nonsense," said Branwell. "I only pretend to her that I believe it."

"There are real things," said Emily, "much harder for me

to believe. It is hard to believe that heaven can be more beautiful than our heath today. Perhaps it is true, what John Brown told Branwell, that the witch of the Moor was a woman. Perhaps she was discontented in heaven and homesick for the Moor, and so the angels threw her back upon it."

Charlotte answered reprovingly:

"The Moor must be dreadful and black compared to the radiance of heaven. You should not suggest such things, Emily!"

There was magic in the afternoon. Charlotte could feel it herself as they went on together over the sunlit hills. Patches of black, as they drew near to them, revealed themselves suddenly as masses of green fern. Pink masses became feathery clumps of ling heather. Sometimes the children came scrambling through clumps of long grass. Sometimes they ran through heather, soft peat ground underfoot giving a bounce to their steps; or they stood still, listening to the sound of the high, chanting wind.

A black-faced sheep started after them, but Branwell turned and made a pass at it. With a frightened bleat it jigged off on its gray, stick-like legs.

They went on more slowly. Their footsteps turned toward their own part of the heath, the warm hollow by Sladen Beck.

They set out the army of the Twelve Adventurers by the waterfall, and wood clashed on wood as they fought, twice over again, the battle of Waterloo. Then Charlotte declared that Napoleon was exiled, and renamed Branwell's soldier "Rogue."

"These"—she picked up two more—"are Captain Tree and Corporal Leaf. And here are Goody and Bady and Naughty and Bravey and Sneaky," she pointed. "They are the twelve finest young men in all Great Britain, brave as lions, all of them, and very powerful."

"Are they as powerful," asked Anne, "as Genii?"

Charlotte hesitated. Then she said:

"It is the Genii who make them powerful. The Genii will send them to the Mountains of the Moon in Africa. They will build a great city with the help of the Genii."

Branwell swept Rogue aloft in his hand.

"Fine! Let them start at once. Sladen Beck is the Indian Ocean and the box is the good ship *Invincible,* manned by the Twelve Adventurers."

Quickly they swept the scattered soldiers together into the box and rigged a sail of tall green ferns. Branwell with a shove of his hands sent out the good ship *Invincible* across the ocean. But the waves were high and the current strong, and the ship came to grief against a rock with the Twelve Adventurers set suddenly afloat on a turbulent sea.

"Get them! Quickly!" Branwell snatched his army from the brink of the waterfall. Charlotte was equal to this occasion.

"They are shipwrecked on the Guinea coast. And we are the Chief Genii who rescue them from shipwreck."

As they set the Adventurers out to dry in the sunlight, Branwell demanded:

"Won't they be attacked by the savages? My geography book says that there are fierce tribes of hostile 'blacks' all over the Guinea coast."

"We are the Chief Genii!" Charlotte repeated. "We will save the Twelve Adventurers from the savages too. We will build a magic city for them in the midst of the Mountains of the Moon."

"Are we all Chief Genii?" questioned Anne. Eagerly Branwell took up the game.

"Of course we are. I'm Chief Genius Branni."

"You mean 'Chief Genie,' Branwell," Charlotte corrected. But Branwell scoffed.

"Pooh! It's easy to see that you know nothing about Latin. 'Genius' is the singular of 'genii,' stupid!"

"Oh, of course. I must have forgotten." Charlotte's cheeks flamed. Even if she did not go to school any more Branwell must not think she had less education than he. Eagerly she turned back to the game.

"I am Chief Genius Talli, and Emily is Chief Genius Emmi, and Anne is Chief Genius Anni . . . and we will ride to the Mountains of the Moon. There we will build the most marvelous city of all time. The glorious, shining, scintillating city of . . . of . . ."

"Glasstown!" Branwell supplied the name.

"And all of the inhabitants," she went on, "shall be our people. And we will watch over them. And we will make their ruler the Duke of Wellington."

Charlotte's eyes were shining. The plan of the new game became clearer to her with every word she spoke. She breathed:

"Oh, Branwell, it's almost as good a play as the *Arabian Nights*. Let it be our own secret play, forever and ever, about Glasstown and the Twelve Adventurers and that we are the four Chief Genii of the Mountains of the Moon."

The wooden army lay scattered among the pink buds of

ling heather at their feet as they went on, without a pause, to plan Glasstown in the Country of the Genii.

Tiny whirring things passed through the tall grasses, gray against the brown rocks. A pale white butterfly lighted on Anne's dress, then on Emily's hand, and flew away again. Clouds rested just above them on the hills, so close they might almost be leaning over to listen to the secrets of the Genii.

At last Charlotte said regretfully:

"We must go home. See how the shadows stretch on Pickels's Hill."

Sladen Beck danced down the rocks. Blue light deepened to lavender on the hills across the Bottom. The shadows of their own hills lay against the opposite ones in amethyst clearness. Anne clung close to Emily.

"Aren't you afraid?"

"Afraid? Of what?"

"Of the witch of the Moor."

Emily said:

"I believe that the witch of the Moor is herself one of the Genii."

They turned to go toward home. Clouds rippled away from the sun in long rosy veils. A hazy golden mist rose mysteriously from the valley. All the Moor was black and heavy beneath the spreading light along the sky.

"I will race you all back!" shouted Branwell. "It's a straight path. Come along, Charlotte."

Through the brightening world about them they ran as if the ever-lightening clouds above lent rose and golden wings to their feet. Not pelting heavily, like boys at play, but lifted in the dream light, as the tread of light paws on the springing heath. A skylark flew above them as if he were part of their company, and then darted up into the clouds to find his own magic again. A sheep bleated softly in wonder at the glory of the earth.

Four together, they turned in at the edge of the lane. They swept past a grim farmhouse, like the vagueness of shadow in a land of unending splendor.

"Tabby is waiting for us. See, she is standing in the doorway of the kitchen."

"Tabby is the Guardian of the Genii."

The Kingdom of the Genii was established.

Chapter Three

SABBATH OF A GENIUS

ANNE traced on the frosted pane of the window with the heat of her finger, against the green twilight of a December afternoon.

"Talli. . . . Branni. . . . Emmi. . . . Anni. . . . Genii."

Hastily she rubbed the lettering out lest Tabby, who was tramping about setting the tea table, might notice it over her shoulder.

An occasional white flake of snow drifted past the window to melt in the black bare garden. Behind her Charlotte was reading aloud from the book which she had brought home that week from the new Mercantile Library in Keighley. It was *Paradise Lost,* horridly illustrated with wood cuts of all sorts of demons and a picture of Adam and Eve being driven with a flaming sword from the Garden of Eden. Charlotte rolled out the massive words:

> "Of Man's first disobedience, and the fruit
> Of that forbidden tree whose mortal taste
> Brought death into the world . . ."

Tabby's voice blared:

"Tea's on th' table, and gettin' cold."

There was the click of Aunt's heeled pattens on the stone stair. She came pattering in to take her place in the dining room. Charlotte flung down her book with an impatient gesture and joined the others at the table. Papa was having his tea served him in the study. The children sipped and talked to each other.

Aunt said nothing. She was not at her best in December, when the pink chill never left her nose and her silk shawl clung closer about her shoulders with every wheeze of the wind. She crumbled a piece of cake between her fingers and drank sparingly of tea.

At last she pushed the cup away from her and bent slightly forward to make an announcement:

"Young ladies! Do not neglect your curl-papers this evening, or any other preparations which may be necessary for tomorrow's proper observance of the Sabbath."

"The Sabbath!" Branwell groaned. "Is it coming so soon again? I cannot believe it."

"It seems as if it were only yesterday," said Charlotte, "that we attended church and Wesleyan meetings, and church again in the evening."

"Weeks," said Emily, "seem to grow shorter and shorter, and Sabbaths longer and longer."

"Branwell! Young ladies!" Aunt reproved. "Shame upon you to speak so of the Lord's Day. You should rejoice on it and be glad."

Anne looked at Aunt's shiny red nose and the gray lines about her mouth. Aunt did not seem to be very "rejoicing" herself. It made Anne miserable even to think about the Sabbath.

Aunt turned to Tabby, who was gathering up the dishes from the table.

"We will place a white napkin about all the large dishes

tomorrow, and lay forks as well as knives and spoons upon the table. Mrs. Greenwood informs me that it is becoming quite the fashion to use forks! If it is possible, Tabby, observe the decorum of the Sabbath by shutting the door quietly behind you as you return to the kitchen!"

Tabby only grunted in answer and went on piling the tea things together.

Aunt addressed herself to the children again:

"Branwell, do not neglect to wash thoroughly behind your ears. And you may wear your new blue velvet trousers and waistcoat, but strive to keep the lace flounce of your collar as clean as possible. Young ladies—the black bombazines!"

"With the plaid sashes?" Charlotte inquired. "May we wear our plaid sashes?"

"What does it matter?" said Emily. "No one will see them. Our pelisses will cover our dresses. It will be too cold in church even to remove our cloaks."

But Aunt reproved:

"The Lord will see them. Yes, certainly wear the sashes. Above all things, do not neglect the curl-papers."

Aunt, having delivered all her instructions for the Sabbath, rose and still shivering clicked away upstairs.

Tabby swept out toward the kitchen. The door closed behind her with a resounding bang.

That night when Branwell stole out from Papa's room and pranced down the hall for his usual good-night to the others, the door of the girls' room was shut against him.

Charlotte's only answer to his pleas and bangs was the opening of the door by a crack and an emphatic refusal which set every papered hair to vibrating.

"I only wish that you were forced to put up your hair in curlers. Then you'd know better than to come bothering us."

"But I've an idea of a play I want to make out, Charlotte. It's about Glasstown and . . ." Here he attempted as sepulchral a whisper as chattering teeth would allow: "And the Twelve Adventurers."

For once the game of the Glasstown personages could not lure Charlotte.

"Tell me of it tomorrow. There will be time before we must go to church. Go away, now. You'll freeze to death. And we are very busy!"

She slammed the door shut with such a fury that she nearly caught his nose in the crack.

Inside the agony of curl-papering proceeded.

"Hold still, Anne! Do not jerk so."

"But you are hurting me. Ouch! Oh, dear, Charlotte, must you pull at me quite so hard?"

"It is the only way to make them tight. There! You have jerked it undone again. If you do not hold still we will never be finished."

All three shivering, they crept between the icy sheets into bed.

"Not that there is any use trying to sleep," groaned Emily, twisting to find a spot for her head. "We'll never sleep in any event, with all these papers prickling us." But a moment later all three slept soundly.

There was not an honest citizen of Haworth who was not an observer of the Sabbath. A few loiterers and drunkards there might be, but such "raffle coppins" kept themselves well out of sight, hidden in long grass on the Moor in the summer, and in winter safe by their own firesides.

At the summons of the bell in the church tower, the cobbles of the street resounded to the clogs of the arriving congregation. Morning, afternoon, and night they came in their best Sunday clothes: mill hands and servant girls, Mr. Heaton on his horse, Mr. Jonas Sugden, mill owner and Wesleyan leader, who walked all the way because he did not consider it according to God's law to make his horse work on the Lord's Day.

On rainy days they came, or when snow piled in high drifts and the winter wind slid knife-like through the heaviest of woolens, to sit for hours in the bare and heatless church. Faithfully, in the summer they came in their best silk waistcoats for the three interminable services.

As for Mr. Brontë, Tabby came knocking at his door when it was still pitch black.

"Time t' get up!"

She slapped down a pitcher of cold water. He had to go early to the schoolhouse to conduct Sunday School for the children, where they were taught to read from the Bible and to write its texts with fingers which had been feeding wool to machines in the mill all week long.

Anne and Charlotte and Emily had to get up nearly as early in order to undo their curl-papers and fix their hair. They combed it forward in tight frizzes exactly like Aunt's false front.

The dresses which Aunt had told them to wear were made of black silk, with long skirt and loose bodice, very low in front and high in back and with ruffled white collar. They pulled their plaid sashes high over their stomachs, and tied them behind in a big bow. Finally they buttoned on their long pelisses, which fell straight to their knees.

They hurried out to go down to breakfast. On the stairs they met Branwell. He was dressed up too, in a short coat like a jacket shining with big gold buttons. Branwell said:

"Well, I have decided to save the play which I was making

out last night. I am going to make it out to myself during the discourse in church this morning."

"I have thought of a good play too, to make out during the discourse," said Charlotte.

"Hush!" Emily warned. "Aunt is already down."

Aunt's Sunday dress was like the girls', of black bombazine. A wide lace shawl had replaced the usual white silk, and wide lace lappets hung from her Sabbath cap, trailing across her black bosom.

Anne felt too full to eat any breakfast. It was all very well for Branwell and Charlotte to close their ears to the discourse. They need not even listen when Papa began to talk about such awful things as "original sin" and of lost souls flying about in the graveyard. The Sabbath could not be so bad for them as it was for her.

Immediately after breakfast they were sent to get ready for church. Tabby had pumped a great bucketful of water for them, in which to wash faces and hands.

In the kitchen they stood splashing away together. Branwell spluttered importantly:

"I am going to have that villain, Captain Tree, plot against the Duke of Wellington, to upset the whole confederacy of the Genii."

"I," Charlotte declared, "am going to have Lord Albert Florian Wellesley conquer Captain Tree in a duel, fought behind the Inn of the Genii, and so save the honor of the noble Duke of Wellington, his father."

They went out through the hallway, chattering to each other on the bend of the stairs.

Aunt pattered out of her room in her black Sunday bon-

net; her face was gray and ghostly under it in the clear sunlight.

"Quiet, young ladies! It is the Sabbath. Such noise is unseemly in the ears of the Lord."

They tip-toed away to their separate rooms. They put on
their own black bonnets and buttoned their cloaks up high
under their chins. Charlotte parceled out the handkerchiefs.

"Here you are, with your initials. Here is E, and here is A,
and here is one for me."

Softly they tip-toed downstairs again.

Anne gave Emily's elbow a tiny squeeze, whispering:

"What will you play, Emily? Will you play, too, during
the service? Will you play about Glasstown?"

"Of course she will!" Charlotte answered for her in a firm
undertone. "All the Genii must play about Glasstown today."

Branwell came up behind them with a hiss that made Anne
jump. In Emily's ear he vibrated a snake-like voice:

"You make out a good play for once, and don't go off
thinking about nothing as you did last week. If I see that
moorhen look on your face again, I shall pinch you!"

There was no chance for an answer, even if Emily had
chosen to give one. Aunt was dangerously impatient at the
doorway.

Branwell ran on ahead to the church. Charlotte walked
sedately beside Aunt. Anne followed behind with Emily. The
fair curls nodded against the dark frizzes.

Their feet made clear prints on the thin new fall of snow,
as they marched down the short stretch of roadway to the
church. The sun shone and glittered on each snow-covered
roof of Haworth lying below them, and away in blue fairy

shine and between the black patches of bog land into the hills, until their eyes were dazzled with the splendid morning.

Branwell waited for them at the doorway of the church, over which the dedication "To Saint Michael" was filled and changed absurdly by wedges of snow.

The first peal of the church bell sounded as they came out of the fine clear morning into the cold, shadowy church. They were just half an hour early. It was Aunt's usual time of arrival; Aunt could not abide tardiness.

As they padded up the aisle, there were just three other people in the church, who turned curiously to examine them. Anne recognized one of them as Mr. Barraclough, the blacksmith, very much washed and in a brave stuff waistcoat, but with a face as red as if he had come this minute from the heat of his forge.

Clear down to the front marched Aunt, and opened the square wooden door which divided the Brontë pew from the main aisle of the church. With a stiff rustle of skirts she swept in before them.

Directly in the center of the church sat Aunt. Not Mrs. Greenwood herself, the wife of the wealthiest mill owner in Haworth, had such a prominent spot. Like a dark coronet, Aunt's tall bonnet uprose directly before the communion table.

After Aunt came Anne and Charlotte and Emily, in order. Branwell sat next to the pew door, which Aunt with a firm hand latched behind them. The back of the pew came just about to the level of Anne's eyes, but if she sat straight up and twisted her head she had a good view of the church and the aisle behind her.

Pacing slowly around the church, even more dignified and aloof than Papa could be, was John Brown. In his hand was a long hickory staff. Anne knew the use of the knob on the end of the pole. More than one sleeper, nodding at Papa's long sermons, had felt it rap on the back of his head and had been brought broad awake. Many a child had been quieted from a bit of restlessness by a shake of John Brown's head or a threatening gesture of the awful staff. Anne, her back almost broken by the strain of sitting straight, felt a prickle on her neck at the very idea of that knob.

Tom Sugden came down the aisle in a tight, high collar, following his father and mother. Branwell winked and made a face at him as his mother turned her back, but Tom pretended he had not seen him and stumbled into the pew after his parents.

The villagers looked strange and unnatural in their tight waistcoats. They walked softly, having taken off at the door of the church the knobby-soled clogs which they wore all week upon their feet. Many of the women had fine lace shawls like Aunt's over their woolen dresses.

There was a brief scurry at the door, but it was only the Rushforth girls whispering and nudging each other. At the back of the church John Brown cleared his throat. Immediately there was silence again.

Anne recognized some of the members of the Haworth orchestra going up into the choir loft, which stretched directly above her head and across one side of the church. It was higher even than the tall reading desk which towered in the pulpit and above the congregation.

There was a sudden silence as a door below the choir loft

opened. Papa strode forth, with the folds of his long black cassock sweeping to the floor.

He stood forward. His voice rang to the stone walls, announcing the name of the first hymn. The trombone in the choir blared it out. The congregation bellowed with a hearty good will:

> "A charge to keep I have,
> A God to glorify,
> A never dying soul to save
> And fit it for the sky. . . ."

High above them, standing at the reading desk, Papa raised both arms like black wings.

"Let us pray!"

The service had begun.

It went on, smoothly enough, until about the middle of the reading of the lesson for the day. Then, suddenly, came a loud interruption.

Clatter! Clatter! Bang!

The congregation nodded and whispered. It was the Sunday School children coming in from the schoolhouse, thumping along in their clogs.

Branwell knew them all. He swerved around to watch them, shoving and jostling at each other to crowd into the last two rows of pews.

Suddenly he grinned, nudging Charlotte, and whispered:

"There is Squire Heaton and the Midgeley's Charity Boys."

At the rear of the Sunday School procession came six boys in spotless brand-new blue suits. Beaming over them with fatherly pride was one of Papa's wealthiest trustees, Squire Heaton of Ponden House.

These lads never stopped at the back with the rest of the Sunday School children, but came marching importantly to the very front, and never paused until they had wriggled into the pew directly under the minister's desk and right before Aunt's own black bonnet.

Once more the congregation nodded and whispered. This time the comment was a brief three words of explanation:

"Midgeley's Charity Boys!"

The Midgeley's Charity Boys were so called because they were boys chosen by the trustees of the church each year to be the recipients of a bequest in the will of a certain David Midgeley. Often Papa had described the generosity of this David Midgeley, who had lived on a farmland high in the lonely part of the Moor called the Withens. In his will he had left the money from the rent of that part of his farms called the Middle Withens to pay for the clothing each year of six boys whose families were too poor properly to afford clothing. The boys were to be clad in "convenient blue clothes." In his will he also made a condition that the fortunate lads should all attend Haworth church on the Sunday before Christmas.

It had become a custom for one of the trustees of Papa's church to give the boys a good dinner after the conclusion of the service of the morning, a feast which had of late fallen to the generosity of Squire Heaton. It was the only Christmas celebration allowed by the Wesleyan Society in Haworth.

The good Wesleyan folks' stern religion forbade that the heathen greeting of "Merry Christmas" should be uttered, or any mention of it, on this cold and snowy Sunday before Christmas Day.

Once more the congregation fell into silence, and the parson was given the attention of the people of Haworth, as he proceeded with the morning service. Anne looked at the boy in front of her fussing with the collar of his blue suit, and wondered how it felt to be a Midgeley's Charity Boy.

Before the sermon the Sunday School children clattered out again to go to their lessons, but the Midgeley's Charity Boys stayed in church. This was their special Sabbath, and they were to sit beside Squire Heaton, beneath Aunt's nose, clear to the end of the sermon hour.

Mr. Brontë closed the Bible and stood up to deliver his discourse. Silence was like a piece of grass pulled out long and strained to the breaking point. Attitudes took listening form. Eyes were turned on the preacher, expectantly.

The discourse had begun.

To Charlotte, to Branwell, and to Emily the booming voice and the moving hand on the pulpit cushion grew suddenly unreal and unimportant. Charlotte's eyes were shining with the visions of Albert, Lord Wellesley, in his crimson furnished room in the Lusiva Palace, and the clash of swords in a golden dawn. Before Papa had reached the end of his introductory remarks her word-pictures would be tumbling into stories.

Emily's eyes were screwed nearly shut, as she sat humped over. Her breath was coming in odd puffs through her nose. She did look a little bit like a moorhen, Anne decided, the way her hair hung over her ears.

The congregation was listening with close attention to every word pronounced from the high pulpit. But the Genii had escaped from their chill, numbed bodies into their own precious country of "making-out."

All the Genii, that is, save Anne. Anne, turn and twist as she would, could not escape the clear sound of the preacher's voice. There was Branwell frowning, and Charlotte's very lips forming words of her own, and Emily drifting away to some nice and summery, warm-smelling hollow on the Moor. But for Anne not even a picture would form itself to blot out Papa's face and his long, shaking finger. If only she could think of something else, of what they had played yesterday, of the words of the rhyme Charlotte had composed.

Suddenly the flat palm of the preacher's hand slapped on the open Bible before him. Anne jumped.

"He that hath ears to hear, let him hear!"

Surely the dark eyes were focused directly upon her as he spoke the words. She could feel them to the bottom of her feet. She swallowed and choked, and looked away from the rest of the dreaming Genii directly at the pulpit. With both ears she began obediently to listen.

"And the tenth unforgivable sin . . ."

On and on it went for a trembling, aching hour, while the Midgeley's Charity Boys squirmed and wriggled, to Aunt's intense annoyance and in spite of all the threatening faces which John Brown could contrive or all that the firm hand of Squire Heaton could do.

Then, just as it seemed that Papa was never going to stop, he paused. The black wings of his arms were extended once more above the congregation:

"And now, O Lord, as we conclude this service . . ."

The pews squeaked together as the people of the congregation bent reverent heads.

"Let us sing. . . ."

Aunt sprang up instantly. The choir shuffled to its feet in the loft above for the hymn of dismissal.

> "Before Jehovah's awful throne
> Ye nations bow with sacred joy,
> Know that the Lord is God alone,
> He can create, and He destroy."

Outside the church Jonas Sugden and Mr. Greenwood and Mr. Heaton crowded about Papa, commenting upon his discourse.

Aunt marched out looking neither to left nor right. She walked with bristling stride through the crowds and ordered the children along with her.

Branwell followed reluctantly. He would far rather have stayed behind to attempt a word with Tom Sugden or John Brown, but Aunt commanded:

"Branwell! No loitering, or you will receive no Yorkshire pudding for your dinner!" Promptly he obeyed her and ran before them all, scuffing up the snow in clouds of white brilliance behind his heels.

The children stayed in the snowy garden for the few precious moments left before dinner time. Scarcely had the door closed upon Aunt's dignified figure when Charlotte let out a shriek.

"Branwell. . . . You brute! You've put snow down my neck!"

They were off across the snow in a panting race, Anne and Emily joining in the pursuit of the more agile boy, forgetful of the Sabbath, forgetful of their good clothes, forgetful of everything save the pleasure of being able to run and jump with their stiffened limbs.

They surrounded Branwell at the wall at last, and came down in a laughing heap on a snow bank, rolling gaily upon each other. A sudden voice startled them.

"Have a care, Children of Sin! Satan is not idle, but idle play profanes the Sabbath."

It was Papa, come home from church. They leaped to their feet in thorough confusion. Charlotte found presence of mind enough to say:

"Good afternoon, Papa."

He strode past them without replying, and into the house.

"Hurry, now," Charlotte ordered. "And make ready for dinner or Papa will be down before us."

"Good for dinner!" Branwell sang out. "I'll race you all round to the pump. Come along, Emily!"

Papa managed Tabby's roast and excellent Yorkshire pudding with a hearty appetite. He did not seem a bit tired from his long hour of shouting.

He had brought a book of the sermons of John Wesley to the table with him. It was propped up before him as he ate. The reading of the newspaper was forbidden on the Sabbath. Over the pudding he raised his head suddenly, to inquire of Aunt:

"You will surely attend the meeting in the Wesleyan chapel, this afternoon, Miss Branwell? Ah, that is well. I am glad to do all in my power to encourage the good work of the Wesleyans."

"Possibly," Aunt suggested, "you will want to accompany us to the Wesleyan meeting, Mr. Brontë!"

But when they started, promptly at three o'clock, to walk to the Wesleyan chapel, Papa was not of their number.

The stark plainness of the roughly built Wesleyan chapel was a sharp contrast to Papa's church. There were no stained-glass windows or carved stone arches in the Wesleyan chapel. It was the barest sort of room, with a square door and small slits for windows and plain, unpainted wooden benches.

The Wesleyan chapel had been built, stone upon stone shaped and laid and aligned, by the hands of the loyal Wesleyans. Not a stick of furniture had been bought, but all had been made. Each man, mason, carpenter, or blacksmith, made that at which he was most apt. Each gave freely of his service to complete the chapel.

Aunt had seen the beginnings of the Wesleyan Revival Movement in her own youth, golden in recollection, in Cornwall near Penzance. Her own uncle, John Fennel, the great-uncle of the children, had been a Wesleyan preacher before he had become a regular minister of the Church of England, like Papa.

Aunt sat as far at the back of the Wesleyan meeting as she sat forward in the church service.

"The seats directly before the leader," she would explain patronizingly, "are for such ignorant and lowly persons as the spinners and woolcombers from the factories, who are in continual danger of moral backsliding, persons whose souls are as yet unsaved."

Anne, sitting beside Aunt and watching the woolcombers and the spinners clatter into their places, wished that she could be as sure as Aunt that her own soul was saved. She moved closer to Emily, who sat beside her, and listened to the banging door, the clattering clogs on the stone floor, and the cheerful unrestrained gabble of voices about her.

There seemed at first to be no one to lead the meeting, but
when they had been sitting there for about five minutes, suddenly up rose a tall, hatchet-faced man. Anne shivered. He
looked, to her mind, uncannily like Satan himself. It was
Jonas Sugden, owner of a large worsted mill on the road to
Keighley. Above the hubbub and clatter he shouted:

"Friends, it's time t' hold th' meetin'!"

The clattering fell silent. Aunt looked down the bridge of
her nose condescendingly upon Mr. Sugden, as he roared
once more:

"We will now sing: 'When young, prepare yourself to die.'
Give us the pitch, Tim o' Sim's!"

A moment later the four Brontë children were shouting
from memory, with the rest, the words of the familiar hymn:

> "When young, prepare yourself to die,
> For life is short and death is nigh.
> In youth and strength put to your craft.
> The strongest living is but daft."

At the conclusion of the hymn, Jonas Sugden bellowed:

"Now we will have prayers. Who is moved by the Lord to
offer th' prayer in our meetin' this even?"

A white-haired, thick-set man jumped to his feet.

"I am, Mr. Sugden."

"Proceed, Mr. Shackleton!"

After Mr. Shackleton two or three more rose to offer
prayer. There was another hymn; then Jonas Sugden announced:

"If there is none else who desires to offer prayer, there is
summat I'm bound by th' Lord to tell ye, friends!"

There was a creaking of benches as many leaned forward, curious to hear what their leader had to say. Anne listened dry-mouthed and trembling, as the preacher's voice played like thunder about her. Jonas warmed to his subject.

"Friends! I want to tell ye, all of ye, summat as happened to me one Sabbath afternoon. And praise th' Lord that I came home by th' way of Oxenhope and not ower th' Moor as I do by custom. Friends, as I was comin' down th' road I saw a breaker o' th' Sabbath, workin' with pick and shovel. It were John Taylor, friends, a woolcomber in my own mill. John Taylor breakin' th' Sabbath by workin' in his oat field on this holy day!"

A shocked gasp spread like a whisper over the congregation. The Brontë children sat up, eager to hear the rest of the tale. Sabbath-breaking was known to be one of the unforgivable sins that would keep you out of heaven. With chattering teeth Anne watched Jonas's gleaming eyes as he told of his interview. Vividly Jonas described his own lecture to the sinner.

"Th' eternal hell fire and torment t' follow. . . ."

Anne could almost hear the man's shriek of terror as he threw down his shovel and fell on his knees before Jonas, begging for mercy. Jonas waved a dramatic finger before the meeting.

"Friends, I tell ye yon sinner sweat from head to foot before the terrible Judgment of the Lord which I made plain to him! And see, friends, what the devil has in store for all sinners who have not declared for heaven!"

The very breathing of his listeners was stilled as Jonas, with glittering eyes and husky voice, pictured the demons and the little red tongues of leaping flames waiting thirstily for unsaved souls.

At this moment a man jumped like a frightened rabbit into the air, shrieking at the top of his lungs.

"I declare! I declare for heaven!"

Anne looked up, startled. If a bee had stung the man he could not have leaped more suddenly! But, having said his say, he sat down once more, listlessly, and Jonas continued as before.

Someone whispered in a husky undertone:

"They do na' count him much. He declares nigh onto each Sabbath, and is drunk again, come Tuesday even, at th' Black Bull." Since there were no more "declaring" Jonas said:

"We will end th' meetin' by singin'."

The second long ordeal of the Sabbath was over. Tea was a blessed refreshment. Hungrily the children drank milk and ate bread and oat-cakes.

Aunt told Papa:

"You would have been enlightened, Mr. Brontë, had you attended the Wesleyan meeting this afternoon."

He peered at her over the top of his tea cup.

"Ah, was the meeting led by Mr. Sugden? A godly man to be sure, one who is doing the Lord's work here in Haworth." Papa tipped back his chair and sat down his empty cup, remarking: "It is a positive fact that my church fees have been more easy to collect since Jonas Sugden has become the leader of the Wesleyans."

The seven o'clock service in the church was a long repetition of the morning except that by this time the children were too tired in mind and in their poor cramped limbs to make up any play at all.

At nine o'clock by the high cased clock at the curve of the stairway Papa called them all, Tabby included, to his frigid study across the hall. It was the daily hour of evening prayers, not to be omitted even after the three long services of the Sabbath.

That he should have chosen the longest psalm of the Bible to read tonight was a mystery of torture to his shivering family. Poor Aunt, shuddering under her Sabbath shawl, drew it up to her neck again and again with a despairing jerk. The girls burrowed their hands up to the elbows in the long woolly sleeves of their pelisses for warmth. Branwell pounded his feet on the floor so they could all hear him. Only Tabby seemed not to notice the cold; her big hairy arms were entirely bare, her hands lay folded reverently and calmly together in her lap, as Papa's voice rolled on and on to the hundred and fourteenth verse.

Then came the prayer, and they all had to kneel shuddering on the bare stone floor as Papa thanked the Lord for every separate mercy including the bishops of the church, the king, and "our unfortunate Prime Minister, who is bringing this country to disaster." Papa's mind was turning, at the close of the Sabbath, from church doctrines to the week-day pursuit of politics.

That night in the girls' room three worn-out creatures undressed. Too weary even for an exchange of words, they tumbled into bed. Anne ached with tiredness. Her head and her arms were sore from sitting still. But her eyes were wide open and sleepless in the darkness.

Bit by bit Jonas Sugden's talk of the afternoon came back to her; the picture he had drawn so clearly of the devil with his green eyes. Suppose she should die this minute, would she go to that awful place he had described where you were burned in a fire, just like Tabby doing the roast for Sabbath dinner? And Branwell and Emily! Would they go there too? Charlotte was good and careful, helped Aunt with the table, and sewed in neat little stitches. Charlotte would be safe for heaven. Branwell did so many disobedient things and Papa had to punish him so much that it seemed as if it would be very hard for him to find the way: Branwell had a way of apologizing and getting right with Aunt and Papa after it was all over. Perhaps he would get right with the Lord that way too, just in time, at the end.

But Emily did not get right with people!

Anne lay with burning eyes on the shadows of the ceiling and felt a cold perspiring terror lest Emily, with her proud, dark head and independent eyes, should not let go her soul, even to God.

The shadows began to move in weird circles, reflected in the snow light through the window on the bare walls. There was something bright over in the corner. Perhaps it was one of the ghosts Charlotte had been reading about in *Paradise Lost,* one that had got lost out of the graveyard and was coming in after her. It was swaying to and fro. Those shadowy lines were a skeleton. And the swishing noise in her ears was the melancholy chant of ghostly laughter calling her to the grave to the dreadful Judgment of God! It heaved toward her in a long line.

Desperately she flung back the covers. Where were Emily

and Charlotte? She must get to them. At once, before it was too late, before the skeleton could lay an icy claw upon her.

Onto the freezing stone floor, she plunged on her bare feet. Across the room a head raised itself. It was a horned creature, black and fierce and terrible. It was in Charlotte's and Emily's bed. Shivering and icy-hot Anne stood.

"Anne, whatever are you doing? Get into bed!" Emily's voice was a sleepy and irritable whisper. Relief flowed back into Anne like a warm sweet river. The very crossness of Emily was normal and reassuring.

"I . . . I was scared," she panted an answering whisper. "I thought it was a ghost, or the Judgment Angel, or the witch of the Moor."

"Where? What are you talking about?" Emily's feet were on the floor now. Her voice was still a whisper so that Charlotte would not be roused.

"There! In the corner!"

Even as she pointed she realized that there was nothing in the corner save the faint white reflection of the snow.

"The witch of the Moor would never come into this stuffy house! Move over. I'm coming to get in bed with you."

With the warm nearness and comfort of Emily's body at her side Anne slept, untroubled by foreboding of the coming Judgment.

The ordeal of the Sabbath was over for another long week.

Chapter Four

THE CHIEF GENII CHOOSE
THEIR ISLANDS

1827—another winter. Winter followed winter in quick
succession in Haworth. Scarcely was Christmas followed by
spring and spring by the blessing of summer when November
came moaning down the Moor again to the doors of the parsonage. The Brontës looked from their windows to see that
another year had passed to another December.

But when winter closed in, threatening with snow, Tabby
defied it from her great open fireplace in the kitchen. Tabby's
fire was made of great lumps of peat, squares of grassy sod
dug out of the Moor, set on the precious coals. The black
rectangles themselves gave forth a glowing aura of heat.
There was hissing and snapping of the dried heather roots in
them as they caught fire and flamed up from time to time.
So closely was one flat sod set beside another that they gave
the appearance of a glowing magic carpet. Over the nap of
molten gold, suspended from a great iron hook, hung the
sizzling roast.

The juicy roast gathered heat, it began to sputter, it filled
the kitchen with a good and hungry smell as its juice dripped
down toward the red flames. The smell brought Branwell
down from Papa's room where he had been sitting all afternoon cramping his hand over a drawing of Captain Tree, and
made Charlotte lift her eyes from a poem which she was writing about winter, and sigh, and sniff, and come down to find

what it was all about. It brought Anne and Emily in from the
frozen garden where they had been scattering crumbs for the
starving winter birds, with numb fingers.

"Go clean thy shoon!" Tabby ordered Emily. "Tha' hast
made tracks o' muck on th' floor."

Emily scraped her boots as best she could on the door step
and came back to join Charlotte and Branwell and Anne.
They watched Tabby kneeling, with her full gray skirt spread
over the floor about her. She kept winding a long handle to
turn the roast on the spit around and around, every side of it
toward the red heat. She stood up and went to fetch a big
pan, and put it down on the hot sods of the fire. As the pot
began to get hot, the drops fell into it, sizzling gaily.

From the out-kitchen Tabby now brought in a bowlful of
eggs. She got out the big green earthenware mixing-bowl
from the cupboard.

"What is it?" Branwell asked for the tenth time. "What are
you making for supper?"

"Tha'lt see!"

Emily stood on the rungs of a chair by the window watching, as Tabby broke another egg against the side of the bowl.
Her huge hairy arm kept up a steady beating in firm un-
broken rhythm.

Finally she stopped beating; she lifted the big bowl to carry
it over to the hearth.

She knelt down on the stones, leaning over toward the
flames so far that it seemed her glowing face must be on fire.
Stretching the bowl at arm's length she poured its golden
contents into the drip-pan beneath the spluttering roast.

"Yorkshire pudding!" Charlotte proclaimed.

"Yorkshire pudding it is!" said Branwell. "Why did you not tell us so in the first place, Tabby!"

The woman made no answer, going on with her preparations for supper.

They stood watching the yellow, puffing mass, as drop after drop sizzled down upon it to spread bronze splotches on the creamy pudding.

Emily turned from the window to announce:

"Here comes Papa. He is striding fast up the road. He is almost to the Black Bull Inn!"

Charlotte came up beside her to see out of the window.

"How cross he looks! Where do you suppose he has been?"

"Oh," said Branwell. "He has been visiting some minister or other in Stanbury. I think it was Mr. Saunders, the Baptist minister."

"Aye!" Tabby grunted. "There is naught like wrestling with th' devil t' sharpen th' parson's hunger!" She bent once more to the fire.

Papa came in with great whirl and bluster, stamping his feet, and pulling his ulster and his black greatcoat with its three-layered capes from his shoulders. He was growling to himself, something about "Saunders . . . unreasonable . . . Whig sympathizer!"

The girls pounded upstairs to get ready for supper. It would be an event to have both Papa and Aunt eat with them in winter. If Aunt was not confined to her room with her neuralgia, Papa was generally away from home, or else he would decide to eat his supper by himself in his study.

Emily made a clear place on the windowpane where the frost had misted it into fernlike patterns of white crystals.

"It is too bad," said Charlotte, "that Mr. Saunders is such a Whig! He should be a good Tory like Papa and rise to the standard of the Duke of Wellington!"

But Emily was saying:

"It was snowy white through the fields today. There was ice on the tall grass and crusted on the heather. It was almost too bright to see in the sunlight."

Charlotte stopped brushing her straight brown hair long enough to answer her.

"I should think you would be an icicle yourself after all the time you were out."

"I am an icicle, I believe," said Anne. Her face was gray, almost white, in the chilly light. It was so cold in the heatless room that the breath of each misted in the air.

"It is like white smoke from the nostrils of real Genii!" Charlotte declared. "Here, Anne, let me brush your hair. Emily, fix your bodice. It is buttoned entirely wrong. Aunt will be angry if you appear so at supper."

The brush clattered from Anne's numb hands to the floor. Charlotte, with a final smoothing of her own hair, bent to pick it up. Anne murmured, between blue lips:

"My hands are so cold brushing I couldn't even feel the handle."

Charlotte's hands, more schooled to the cold than hers, did it in double-quick time. A few more minutes and they were all on the way downstairs. The door of the room closed against the cold inside.

Papa came to supper with his cravat billowing almost to his ears. He wore a tasseled nightcap over his thinning hair.

Aunt coughed, cleared her throat, and asked:

"Oh, heavens, Mr. Brontë, do you suppose that this unbearable weather will never cease? Surely we shall all be congealed to corpses before summer's arrival." She sniffed, wiping her pink nose on her handkerchief. "In Penzance where my care-free girlhood was spent we were accustomed to consider that spring was on its way by the end of February."

Papa lifted his head and looked about the table, his eyes piercing through first one then the other of them, to the dark walls of the room behind them.

"The Moor," he pronounced, "is merciless. Perhaps this very night some poor traveler's soul will be required of him, as he lies lost and helpless at the foot of Ponden Crag not three miles from our door. Next spring it may be that you will stumble over the skeleton as you go to gather blossoms upon the Moor."

"Oh!" shrieked Aunt. "Mr. Brontë, I beg of you. My snuff-box! Quickly! Where can it be!" Aunt's nose quivered in the spasm of a sneeze.

Supper ended at last. After supper came evening prayers, in Papa's study. After that they were free to return to the welcome warmth of the kitchen fire and the glowing-tipped peat burning on the hearth.

In a moment they heard Papa leave his study, and the mechanical buzz of the high cased clock on the stairway as he paused to wind it for the night. Sternly he warned the group about the fire:

"Children! Do not stay up too late!"

But a moment later Papa's warning was forgotten; Emily was calling excitedly:

"Look! It is really a snow storm!"

They left the fire to press their noses close against the window and to watch the falling flakes of the storm.

"They're swirling," said Charlotte excitedly, "as if one of the Chief Genii were creating a new palace in Glasstown, of marble and white pearls."

Anne cupped both hands about her eyes and leaned very hard against the window, beside Emily.

"Road will be filled up by morning," groaned Branwell. "I guess they'll have to postpone the wedding of Tom Sugden's sister."

They stood there for several minutes, crouched together. The wind was not so noisy now, but it came around the corner in a long whistle and kicked up the snow into wider and wider circles. When they turned at last, the red glow of the kitchen fire and its gleam on the rafters and the wide table filled them with a sense of coziness and comfort. Tabby, half asleep, nodded over her big black Bible, her square hairy chin sunk deep in her ox-like neck, as peaceful as if the storm were miles away.

"I shall write a poem about the snow," said Charlotte. "I'll fetch my writing desk."

"Let us light a candle," Branwell suggested. "We cannot write well by firelight. There are candles in the drawer of the table." With a jerk, up came Tabby's head. The rocking chair crunched to a standstill.

"Yon candle'll stay in th' drawer this night."

Charlotte protested:

"But, Tabby, Aunt does not forbid our having a light downstairs."

"No matter sinna Miss Branwell say 'aye' nor 'nay.' I tell

thee yon candle'll no be lit!" She added, half mumbling:
"Muckle flicker and wee glow tha'dst have this windy even."
The big mouth closed with a decisive snap over the dark and
hairy chin.

"Oh, dear!" Charlotte admitted. "I suppose that it would
flicker on such a stormy night, and the light would not be
steady enough to write by. I'd not thought of that."

Branwell, yawning, stretched out his trousered legs to the
comfortable heat!

"Well," he said, "I'm sure I don't know what to do."

Tabby's thick voice, like a man's, broke into their silence.

"Ye can all go t' bed!"

Branwell was roused to a retort.

"I'd rather do anything than that."

"Oh, Tabby," moaned Anne. "Whatever makes you so
glum tonight? Such a good night it is for you to tell us a
story!"

"A story! A story!" The rest took up the cry.

"Sing us the ballad of 'Fairy Annie's Wedding'!"

"Na, I canna sing!"

They crowded around her chair, still insisting. Charlotte
and Anne brought stools to sit upon. Emily and Branwell
squatted on the bare stone hearth, looking up into her face.

Soon, in the firelight, while wind slid between the cracks
of the windows behind them and along the floor, Tabby
swayed, chanting the ballad of "Fairy Annie's Wedding."

Her flat, hairy face dipped in and out of the shadows as if
she were weaving a spell upon them. Her cracked voice rose
and fell with the wind, out of the black stillness of night. She
finished the chant in a long, guttural wail.

In the same husky, half singing voice, she asked: "What more shall I tell? What will ye hear?"

They wanted to hear everything she would tell. The glow of the peat fire danced into the deep furrows of her forehead and brown cheeks, and she recited stories and tales and ballads until they hardly dared look into the shadows and the black gleam of the curtainless windows.

On and on her voice rolled, almost as deep and sonorous as Papa's own. She told about the fairies who had held their revels summers ago in the green Bottom where the wind blew gently and the moon shone round and yellow over the hills above. In this protected valley the Moor winds, blowing down from above, lost all their fierceness. Here, in Tabby's childhood, the little folk had danced on bright nights. Tabby herself had seen a fairy one night when she came home too late from milking the kine. Every evening her mother used to set out a brown earthenware bowl of porridge for the wee man who might come to the house at night. And always, mornings, it was found empty, and the hearth was clean swept and a new bright shine was on the pots along the walls.

"Tell about the woolen mills," urged Branwell. "And the time the hand weavers rioted, and tried to keep the mills from being built."

Tabby stirred at the mention of the great smoke-belching factories, new since her time, on the road from Keighley to Haworth. A fiercer gleam seemed to glitter in her black eyes. Her voice sank to the muttering of a far-off storm.

"Th' woolen mills! 'Twas they as drove fairies from th' Bottom." At last she said:

"There. I'll not tell more."

Slower and slower creaked the rockers of Tabby's chair as Tabby herself sat with her hands locked peacefully across her stomach, her head nodding over the big Bible. Snow and hail rattled fitfully against the windows. The wind blew draftily outside the circle of firelight. Within the circle the Genii drew closer together.

"Let us make out a play!" It was Charlotte whispering. "Let us suppose we had each an island, an island to possess, each for our very own."

"Where shall we have them?"

"Anywhere. We may choose any island in the whole world. By the power of the Genii!"

"And what shall we do with them?"

"We will live there, each on our own island. And we will have great men live with us."

Branwell said:

"If I could have any island in the world, I would choose the Isle of Man. And I should take with me . . . let me think now. Whom should I take with me? Oh, I know! I will have John Bull."

"John Bull is a silly person," Charlotte protested.

"I shall take him just the same. And . . . and Astley Cooper. He is not a silly person. I have read about him in the *Manchester Guardian*. And Leigh Hunt! There, that will make enough. We shall have a fine time painting and sketching all day long. And, I declare, we will make a rule forbidding females to set foot upon the Isle of Man."

"Not even if they are Genii?" demanded Charlotte indignantly.

"Not one! Not a petticoat!"

She pulled down the long skirt of her frock suddenly over an exposed white length of pantalets.

"Well, you will find it very dull without us, I am sure!" she said. "My island will be much nicer. I am going to have the Isle of Wight. And the Duke of Wellington shall reign over it with his two sons: the Marquis of Douro and Lord Wellesley!"

Anne said she had chosen the island of Guernsey.

"It will be peaceful and pleasant there. Everyone will be happy all the time. And there will be nothing to fear, ever."

"That is nice," Charlotte approved. "It should be a splendid place for political economists. Lord Bentinck and Sir Henry Halford would like it on your island."

She turned to ask Emily:

"Where is your island? What place will you choose?"

Emily had drawn back into the shadow of the dying firelight. The cold wind seemed to slide between her and the sound of Charlotte's voice. Charlotte spoke again:

"You could have the Isle of Arran. And you could take with you Walter Scott and Johnny Lockhart. Will the Isle of Arran be yours, Emily?"

But Emily could hardly hear. She was listening to the brushing of the wind. Her eyes were on the snow and the white sleet against the window.

"Emily!" Anne gasped. "Emily, what is wrong with you, to make you look like that? What do you see?"

Emily, answering, felt herself part of the wind and the white sleet.

"I don't know. I can't explain it. But it is there at the window. He is there telling me to come out with him over the heath, to the highest of the hills. It is like someone crying, some little animal crying for help on the Moor."

Her hand pointed. A long, twisting serpent of snow hurled, splintered with sleet, against the windowpane. Beyond it a hand was beckoning. Eyes were gleaming, piteously. Or could it be the last faint reflection of the fire mingling with the snow?

Charlotte's hand clutched Branwell's elbow. She said:

"It is one of the little folk. It is a fairy."

Anne had covered her face with her arms. Emily saw a white hand pulling at the window frame. She half rose to go toward it, to fling the window wide, to seize the white cold hand in hers.

"Emily, where are you going? What are you doing?" Charlotte called. Her hand came down hard on Emily's.

Slowly Emily turned. Slowly her eyes looked into those of her sister.

"No matter!" she said. "He is gone now, and I can never follow." Behind them Tabby gave a great snore, waking up.

"Are ye no' t' bed!" The woman blinked and got heavily to her feet. Very deliberately she walked across to pull out the drawer of the kitchen table. She held up a thick, white tallow candle.

"I'll light it!" offered Branwell eagerly.

He knelt down with it at the faded embers. There was hardly enough fire to light it. Ah, there it was! And how it glowed! Nearly enough to blind them.

Slowly, fearfully, they looked back at the window, their courage renewed by the light. The apparition was gone.

"It never was there," scoffed Branwell, as the procession

started upstairs to bed. "It was nothing at all. Only Emily's imagination."

The candle sent wobbling shadows over the slabs of the stone steps. They rounded the turn beneath the high cased clock. Charlotte's hand was still shaking. She insisted:

"But I saw it. It was like one of Tabby's little folk. It was a fairy, a real little fairy."

"Yes," said Anne. "It was a fairy! Was it not, Emily?"

Emily spoke, the last in line, her hands on the shoulders of Anne.

"I don't know. It was hard to see who he was, and hard to hear his voice. But he had a message. . . ."

"A message!"

The flame of the candle leaped in a long jet and a twisted wisp of smoke, as the procession whirled about.

"What sort of message?" whispered Anne.

Emily smiled her long slow smile; her eyes shone in the candle light as if she saw a vision. She answered:

"A message from an island, my island, on the Moor!"

Chapter Five

THE MISSIONARY BASKET

ALL England was holding its breath in the early days of January 1828. The cabinet of Lord Goderich, successor to Lord Liverpool, had fallen while the Duke of Wellington was on the Opposition benches in the House of Lords.

Papa paused in the doorway of Aunt's room to inform her for the twentieth time:

"The new prosperity of England is secure. There is no doubt but what the king will ask the Duke of Wellington to take over the reins of government as Prime Minister."

But Aunt looked up from her inspection of the girls' morning stint of sewing, shaking her head ominously to voice for the twentieth time a pessimistic doubt.

"Mr. Brontë, I do not believe that the Duke of Wellington will accept the prime ministry. There is a great deal of opposition to the Duke of Wellington among the people and in Parliament itself. And was it not only last year that the Duke said himself that he would be mad to think of such a thing?"

"It is a task," said Papa, "for which only the Duke of Wellington is fitted in these troublous times. He must accept! He will accept!"

Papa, having delivered himself of these sentiments, strode off to his study.

Charlotte turned back reluctantly to the work of the morning. Politics was getting to be as thrilling as the plays of the

Islanders and the Twelve Adventurers, now that they were so concerned with the person of the Duke of Wellington. But the tensest political situation of the country could not alter the rules of the household.

It was Aunt's decree that every day the girls should do a certain amount of sewing and mending or dressmaking under her keen guidance. Daily they had to take their places on the big slippery-seated chairs in her room. Daily they stitched, with eyes bent close to their work, in the dull light stealing through Aunt's heavily curtained window.

Sometimes as they worked, the effort of sitting still caused little teasing pains to dart up their backs and into their eyes. Legs dangling hopelessly above the floor on the high-seated chairs became numb and heavy. With dark monotonous rhythm the velvet hangings of Aunt's bed bellied and swayed toward them in the draft. In winter the rattle of the window-panes beat an accompaniment of maddening bumps and jars to their own soft-voiced conversations. Aunt said:

"A young lady whose voice is so clear as to be distinguishable in the next room is in my opinion indecently like a young gentleman."

And then, just as they thought they would surely fall off their chairs, would come the welcome words of dismissal.

"That will be enough for today, young ladies. Fold up your work carefully and replace your needles ready-threaded in your work boxes."

The girls were working painfully, under Aunt's eye, to form the tiny stitches of samplers, each with an elaborately embroidered Bible selection.

Charlotte had nearly completed hers, but Emily's was far

from done. She had chosen for her Bible verses the thirtieth chapter of *Proverbs*.

Surely I am more brutish than any man, and have not the understanding of a man. I neither learned wisdom, nor have the knowledge of the holy.

Aunt exclaimed in vexation at her choice:

"It is not the proper sentiment for a young lady to talk of being 'more brutish than any man.' " To which Emily replied:

"It is in the Bible!" And Aunt could not gainsay her.

Anne was only beginning to do her sampler. She had chosen from the shops in Keighley, with Aunt's aid, bright soft silken thread to make the pattern of the cross-stitch.

Whatever they worked upon, whether embroidery or fancy work or the darning of one of Branwell's coat pockets or Papa's hole-ridden socks, Aunt insisted upon absolute perfection of workmanship in the delicate, almost imperceptible stitches which she made them take.

In her own claw-footed chair Aunt sat bolt upright. Her back never touched the horsehair padding.

"No lady," Aunt would tell them daily, "would ever allow herself to relax save in her bed or possibly in a swoon, should occasion arise."

Today, first of all, Charlotte had been set to cutting to pattern the pieces for day-time dresses for the three girls. The material, spread out on the wide bed, was dark green woolen stuff purchased from Mr. Eccles, one of the hand-loom weavers in the village.

Aunt and Charlotte undertook to cut from the whole piece the big shapes for the sleeves and skirts which would fall nearly

to their ankles, revealing the lacy bottoms of their long pantalets. This was rendered all the more difficult by the fact that
Papa, being taken one time by fear lest an accident might
occur to one of the children, had carefully ground off the
points of every pair of scissors in the house.

Anne worked upon her sampler and Emily was set at the
darning. Between stitches Aunt heard their geography lesson
for the day.

Papa had gone to Bradford himself and purchased the
geography book which they were using. Page by page the girls
learned it. Page by page they recited back to Aunt such por-
tions as:

"Jersey, Guernsey, Alderney, and such, are small, populous
Islands near the coast of France," or: "Elephants, rhinoceroses,
buffaloes, tigers and wild oxen, deer and antelopes are numer-
ous in China. But hares, wolves, sheep, lions, camels and asses
are not to be met with," or: "America was discovered by
Cristóbal Colón, somewhere near the end of the fifteenth
century."

"Must we learn the pictures also?" asked Anne. "Or are they
only to be regarded?"

Sternly Aunt replied:

"My dear Anne, the pictures are fully as important as the
lists of the principal cities. They should be learned to the
finest detail, so that when you are grown and visit these foreign
countries, you will find it no surprise to land in New York
and be greeted by a dark creature with feathers in its hair and,
I blush to say, not sufficient garments upon its body."

Charlotte turned over the pages of the geography to the
picture of the swarthy Indian with two large feathers shooting

up out of his lank jet black hair. Shuddering she asked:

"Do they never wear clothes? Not even the butcher and the baker?"

Emily leaned over to untangle a knot in her sewing.

"I think it would be nice to dress like the Indian in the picture. Then we would not have any mending to do, ever!"

Aunt swooped upon her.

"Emily, the condition of your work is a positive disgrace.

Surely the darning of a woolen sock cannot be so difficult as you make it. Permit me to see your work!"

Emily delivered up the hopeless tangle of thread: Papa's sock, full of holes from his long tramps to Keighley and back. Aunt bent to inspect it, severely disapproving.

At this moment came three sharp raps in succession on the big oaken front door downstairs.

"I . . . I'll go," Emily gulped, half rising to escape from Aunt's bright-eyed scrutiny and her increasing frown. "I'll answer that knock!"

"You will do nothing of the sort!" Aunt's eyes narrowed to the arch of her nose. "It is always considered the place of a servant to wait upon the door, certainly not that of a young lady of the house."

But the knock had to be repeated before they heard Tabby's clogs clattering, going in answer to the summons, and the scratch of the door opening against the step.

A female voice addressed Tabby. The girls, poised over their work, listened intently to discover the woman's errand.

She stated it with the brief words:

"Mrs. Heaton's compliments, and she says, please, ma'am, it's Miss Branwell's turn now with the missionary basket. So here be it."

Charlotte's scissors dropped suddenly to her lap. Quickly she looked at Aunt.

"Oh, it does seem soon again. Can it have been all the rounds of the ladies, do you suppose, Aunt?"

"It is," Aunt answered grimly, "exactly six months ago from next Wednesday since we worked with our hands the last articles of infants' wear which were sold to John Barraclough to cheer his bachelor establishment; and it is six months since I sent his money, together with the rest we had collected from our sales, to the Wesleyan Missionary Cause, and since I sent the basket, with my own compliments, to Mrs. Taylor of Pickels's Hill that she might sew more for the same good purpose."

A moment later Tabby appeared with the basket in her arms. It was a deep, oval willow basket with round, hooped handles, dedicated to the purpose of conveying from house to house in Haworth a collection of such things as pincushions, card-racks, or infants' wear, which decorated the mantel of John Barraclough's one-room blacksmith forge.

These were wrought with care by the Christian ladies of Haworth parish and sold to those gentlemen who could not escape. From mill owners to worsted spinners, none was exempt from the beguiling females who worked for the missionary basket.

Each lady had her turn at working for the basket. Aunt, who was perhaps as active in this cause as any, took her full share of the burden, both sewing and selling. To the girls it seemed that the missionary basket was constantly reappearing at the door of Haworth parsonage.

Tabby flung it down at Aunt's feet.

"Here's th' basket come again!"

It was generally understood that the proceeds of the basket went principally for the conversion of the heathen and such other non-Christians as might be classed under this title.

"It looks," murmured Anne, "most dreadfully empty, and as if it will take a great many pincushions to fill it."

"Why not," Charlotte suggested, "fill it with babies'

blankets? They are quite bulky and would fill up the basket in no time."

Grimly Aunt's eyes swept the three faces turned woefully upon the willow basket at her feet. She sat even more perpendicular to the seat of the horsehair chair than before. In all the majesty of her large frame, her big jaw thrust slightly forward, she lectured them:

"Do you realize, young ladies, that this work may reach in its power to furthest Africa? Can you imagine all the souls that may die in the torment of everlasting fire because of your slackness? Young ladies, what is faith without good works?"

When the missionary basket entered the door of the parsonage all other work had to be put aside. Aunt ordered, not without a choke of regret in her voice:

"And now you may carefully fold together your samplers. We shall resume that task at another time, when the work of the Lord does not stand waiting!"

Papa did not join them at tea that night. He shut himself into his study with the *Leeds Intelligencer* and every issue of the *Manchester Guardian* for the last three months. He was trying to discover for himself the answer to the question which was being put at every tea table in the country. Who was to be the new Prime Minister? He came stamping across the kitchen doorway and roared out an order to Tabby:

"I shall have my supper served alone in the study. And with plenty of mutton!"

The next day, work on the missionary basket was begun in earnest. Directly after breakfast Emily was sent to Miss Craven's shop, opposite Mr. Barraclough's forge, to purchase a bit of ribbon to be made into the needle-books. Some old stuff was found in the garret to use for the infants' clothing. And the sewing began!

The black stuff found in the garret proved only a beginning of the material that they would need. Charlotte and Anne were told to put on their warm woolen cloaks and fasten thick clogs on their feet instead of the low shoes they wore indoors, and to go down to Mr. Eccles, the weaver, for a length of cloth. Aunt stipulated:

"Woolen goods! Ask Mr. Eccles for a length of wildbore."

In the parsonage not one article of linen or cotton clothing was allowed. That was Papa's order. Papa was positive that there was great danger of these materials' catching fire.

Mr. Eccles lived just below the Fleece Inn, in a two-and-a-half-story house. The half-story on top was brightened by many windows. It was Mr. Eccles's workroom.

As Charlotte and Anne came down the street they drew the collars of their capes high about their necks to shut out the gale of sharp wind. The door of Mr. Eccles's house stood wide open, so that they could hear the clip-clip of his loom, busily at work.

Charlotte had to rap twice upon the edge of the open door before Mrs. Eccles heard and came from the kitchen to receive her, scrubbing-brush in hand.

"Good morning, Miss Brontë. Can I serve thee aught? Is th' parson proper fine?"

Anne held tightly to Charlotte's skirts. Charlotte felt herself growing furious and cold all over at the frank, hard look of curiosity in Mrs. Eccles's hazel-blue eyes. Like many of the village women, she could not well make out the parson's daughters. They were so quiet and queer, and unlike their brother.

Charlotte answered in a strained and distant voice with the very intonation of Aunt.

"Mr. Brontë is quite well, thank you. Aunt would like, please, a length of wildbore, for clothing for the missionary basket."

"I'll take thee to Mr. Eccles."

Mrs. Eccles turned to lead the way up the two flights of dark circular staircase. Behind her stumbled Charlotte and Anne.

They came up at last to the brightness of the low-ceilinged room at the top of the house. There, with his face to the light and his back full upon them, sat Mr. Eccles before his loom. He and his loom and the piles of white, finished goods filled the place so completely that the girls found scarcely room to stand inside the door.

For the moment he did not hear them as he kept throwing the noisy shuttle back and forth, thrusting the woof through the warp with quick motions of his hands, his foot rhythmically working the treadle, adding tiny thread by thread to the clear weave of the cloth.

"Will," Mrs. Eccles's voice rang through the pound of the throttle, "I've brought the Misses Brontë to see thee. They've come on an errand from Miss Branwell, to get a weight o' goods for th' missionary basket."

The pound of the loom ceased momentarily when Mr. Eccles looked about.

"Aunt said," Charlotte spoke up, "that she would like wildbore, if you please."

Mr. Eccles indicated with a sweep of his arm the materials laid upon the floor.

"There's plenty. Take tha pick!" He bent again to his work.

"Oh, thank you." Charlotte fumbled in her little black purse. "How much will it be, please?"

Back and forth moved Mr. Eccles's arm, the fine warp stretching like a white spider-web before him, as the long shuttle plunged back and forth between the fine sturdy threads of wool. As high as a standing man could reach, stood the box-like frame of the loom, built of stout beams of wood. Up and down its length swung the tightly drawn threads of the warp, in and out, weaving in the weft, making cloth to last a lifetime. The cloth must go by the carter, in the morning, to Screw Mill in Utley, and from there to Bradford.

The rattle of the loom never faltered, as Mr. Eccles shouted above the clatter.

"There's no cost to thee. 'Tis my church 'tithes' to th' parson."

Charlotte's feeble thanks were lost in the din, as she knelt to pick out, with Mrs. Eccles's help, a piece of wildbore that might suit Aunt's need and the needs of the basket.

To Charlotte's intense relief Mrs. Eccles did not ask them to stay. It had happened once that she had to sit on the black sofa by the empty fireplace and the faded flowers in Mrs. Eccles's parlor to hear for the whole of an agonized morning about the last moments of Mrs. Eccles's father, who had died in this very room.

With the wildbore in her arms, Charlotte said a hasty good-by and followed by Anne, who had not uttered a single syllable, went plunging out into the street to climb against the mad pushing wind up the road toward home.

They had got as far as Mrs. Rushforth's spice shop, when Anne said suddenly:

"Look! Here comes Branwell. And how fast he is running!"

"He is waving at us!" said Charlotte. "He is trying to tell us something."

Panting, he came abreast of them. He called out:

"Charlotte! Quickly . . . hurry home. A lady is there. She has come to call upon you!"

"To call upon me? What do you mean? I have never had a caller!"

"Well, you have one now, and such a one! You should see her bonnet. It has the appearance of a flower garden! And she came in a carriage with a real coachman driving two horses. Her name is Mrs. Atkinson."

"Mrs. Atkinson? Mrs. Thomas Atkinson? Why, Branwell, that is the name of my godmother. It must be she, indeed."

"Whoever she is, Aunt said to hasten home as fast as you can come!"

Charlotte hurried on up the steep hill. She must slip upstairs to change her dress. It would never do for her to appear before her godmother in a day-time frock.

She was in the house and upstairs almost before she had time to think. She changed in lightning haste to her black bombazine, tying the plaid sash about her waist, fastening a clean ruffle at the back of her collar. She combed her hair smooth, back from the friz across her forehead.

Then she slid downstairs once more.

Softly she tip-toed across the hall to the doorway of the parlor. She pushed aside the curtain and walked in.

Aunt's upright back was toward her. And beyond Aunt, chattering and smiling in Papa's own chair, sat a lady.

She was dressed completely in bright India-red.

Across her shoulders was a shawl, not a white shawl such as Aunt wore, but one gay with a pattern of orange and green embroidered flowers. There were long shining earrings suspended from her ears, and her hair reminded Charlotte of nothing so much as the kinks of a brown poodle dog.

On the back of her head sat an enormous bonnet. Charlotte had never thought that bonnets could be so large and still stay on heads, but this profusion of pink roses and green branches was tied in a firm white bow beneath Mrs. Atkinson's chin.

Aunt was saying:

"Here is my niece, Mrs. Atkinson. Here is Charlotte."

She came forward on deft feet, but her knees seemed to give way beneath her as she bent them to a curtsy before Mrs. Atkinson.

From her lap the lady had lifted a pair of long-handled eyeglasses. She swished forward, peering through them at Charlotte.

"How absurdly the girl is dressed!"

Aunt gasped. Charlotte swallowed. This frock had been made under Aunt's own direction, following the pattern of the finest dress she had worn in her own youth in gay Penzance.

But Mrs. Atkinson went on ruthlessly:

"That skirt is entirely too narrow to be stylish. And such a ruff has not been worn at the back of the neck for many seasons. And the waistline! Really, my dear Miss Branwell." She turned toward Aunt. "Really, it is inconceivable that you are not aware of the present style in the waistline, tight-bodiced and low over the hips. I declare, the girl needs a modesty piece to wear, or a kerchief at her neck. Her bodice is indecently loose!"

Charlotte wished desperately that she might run away and hide. She felt suddenly and completely naked.

Aunt was furious:

"I consider that my nieces are quite suitably attired, Mrs. Atkinson!"

"Ah, well, no doubt you cannot help it. I suppose that in this benighted section of the country the word 'style' is practically unknown."

Mrs. Atkinson beckoned with a long finger to Charlotte.

"Come, god-daughter. Let us hear what you have learned among the woolcombers of Haworth."

Charlotte flushed painfully.

"Madam, I would be ashamed to speak to a woolcomber!"

"Well, I am glad that you are not utterly depraved. Now let us hear what you know of geography. Can you tell me where are the Mountains of the Moon?"

"Yes, ma'am, in Africa!" she answered eagerly.

"Ah. And who discovered the country of America?"

"Cristóbal Colón, ma'am."

"That is correct. What is latitude?"

"Latitude is the distance of a place from the equator toward either pole, reckoned in degrees and minutes." Charlotte quoted from the lessons learned only this noon at such pains from her geography book.

"Well, you are not stupid!" Mrs. Atkinson approved. She suppressed a long yawn. "Perhaps if you were to have education something might yet be made of you."

She turned abruptly, putting up the eyeglasses once more toward Charlotte.

"Would you like to go away to school again?"

Charlotte felt as if something were in her throat to keep her from answering, but her own voice sounded clear in her ears, saying:

"It is what I want most in the world!"

Mrs. Atkinson smiled.

"I am glad of that. I should like my godchild to have ambitions above her surroundings." Her glance shifted to Aunt. "My godchild should associate with the cultured classes of society."

Aunt stiffened. "There are cultured persons in Haworth."

"Folly! My good woman, there can be no culture where there are no noblemen in the vicinity, and none, certainly, where any vulgar mill owner may bray about the doctrines of the church, in the absurd gatherings of the Wesleyans."

"The Wesleyans!" Aunt puffed. "The Wesleyans are doing the work of the Lord in Haworth!"

Her cap was awry, her false front a drunken friz over one eyebrow.

But Mrs. Atkinson answered coolly, unruffled:

"For my part, madam, I think it only too evident that Haworth is a part of the Lord's work which He has overlooked."

She stood up to take her departure, rustling in every broad red fold of the India muslin. The greenery of her bonnet quivered like a bush in the wind from the open doorway.

"Well, it has been a very pleasant visit, I am sure. Will you give my kindest remembrances to my friend, Mr. Brontë? Tell him that it was a disappointment to find him from home; I had hoped to renew our acquaintance. But we must put it off until another time."

She paused, looking down at Charlotte.

"Good-by, my dear. I will recollect to look into the matter of a school for you. You are ambitious and worthy of help."

The door closed behind her. She was gone.

Charlotte's cheeks were burning. She turned. Her eyes sought those of Aunt behind her.

"Aunt, oh, Aunt!" she demanded. "Did she mean it? Do you think my godmother will really send me to school again? Is there even a chance of it, do you think?"

But Aunt's lips were pressed unsmilingly together. She said:

"I should not depend upon it, if I were you. By the time that Mrs. Atkinson has returned to her noble friends at Hartshead she will no doubt have forgotten the vulgar existence of her god-daughter. Absurd gatherings of the Wesleyans! Indeed!"

Before the mirror Aunt paused with an angry jerk to set her cap straight, muttering:

"What right has she to criticize the good people of Haworth!"

It was the first time Charlotte had ever heard Aunt upholding the village of her adoption.

She demanded:

"Where is the woolen goods which you purchased of Mr. Eccles? Bring it at once to my room that we may resume, after this vulgar interruption, the doing of the Lord's work!"

Slowly but surely the basket filled.

While it stayed, all the girls' lessons were suspended. Branwell told them enviously:

"You are in luck. I wish you had seen the lines of Latin I had to learn this morning from Horace!"

Emily's eyes drifted toward the window where streaming

lines of sunset glowed over the black hill. Charlotte looked to the high bookshelf where stood the *Arabian Nights* and *Paradise Lost,* books she had not even opened for a week past.

Emily turned from her brief glance at the wide Moor to say:

"Some day I shall stop sewing suddenly and run off to the Moor and not come back again, ever."

"Oh, Emily dear," Anne remonstrated, and placed a small white hand on Emily's brown one, as they stood by the window for a moment together. "Please do not ever run away from me. I should be so dreadfully afraid without you."

Charlotte and Branwell had settled down near the table with their heads close together.

Charlotte was telling him every detail of her godmother's visit, every motion she had made, every word she had said, finishing with:

"Aunt says that she will surely forget all about her promise to send me to school, but I cannot help hoping and believing, still, that she will remember."

Branwell said:

"Well, I should not want to go away to school. I think so much studying is a waste of time. I would much rather learn to draw portraits. Look, here is a sketch I made this afternoon of one of the Glasstown personages. Do you think it well done? It is the Marquis of Douro!"

He held out the picture for her to see.

"It is splendid!" she told him. "It is the Marquis of Douro, of course. How noble he looks! Oh, Branwell, we must have more of the nobility in Glasstown. We must make it a center for all persons of culture!"

All week the girls stitched on the needle-books and dresses for the missionary basket. Morning and afternoon Aunt pressed them into service, lest Mrs. Greenwood or Mrs. Taylor or Mrs. Heaton dare say that Miss Branwell had not done her duty by the Wesleyan Missionary Cause.

Meanwhile the pink had gone out of Anne's cheeks and there were gray shadows beneath Emily's eyes. Charlotte's own eyes felt hot and heavy with the strain, but as she sat stitching at a needle-book or turning the hem of one of the infant clothes she lived over again the visit of her godmother. Between her and the sewing came the recollection of the pink roses and green foliage of her godmother's huge bonnet. She hoped and hoped again that Aunt might be mistaken in her judgment, that Mrs. Atkinson would not forget her promise to her god-daughter.

At last came the longed-for morning when Aunt said:

"I think we may consider that the basket is full. This afternoon I shall borrow the gig at the Fleece Inn, and John Brown shall drive me throughout the length of this village to seek out such parishioners as are worthy of purchasing our handiwork and contributing to the Wesleyan Missionary Cause."

Three weary Genii escaped and went racing out into the wind of the kitchen garden with entirely unlady-like shrieks, in the pure joy of their liberty.

Next morning Branwell and Papa set off a full hour earlier than usual to fetch the papers from Keighley. Today was to tell the momentous news for which all England had been waiting. Today the decision of the Duke of Wellington would be known.

Charlotte instructed Branwell:

"If it is all right, if the Duke of Wellington is Prime Minister, give the Genii's signal of triumph. Your hand above your head, you know!"

At the same time Papa was telling Aunt:

"In an hour we will know the fate of this nation. May the Lord grant, my dear Miss Branwell, that your forebodings have been groundless." Branwell and Papa made off down the road, striding at a rapid pace in the icy morning air.

The girls cleared the breakfast table and made their beds in a state of keenest excitement. Would Aunt or Papa be right? Would the Duke of Wellington undertake to form the new administration. Would he accede to the request of the king?

Aunt, in pretended unconcern, gave orders about the marketing to Tabby:

"Tell Mr. Pickels that the last quarters of ham which we purchased from him were undoubtedly stringy, and tell him . . ."

The bump of the front door and a loud: "Here we are back!" proclaimed the return of Branwell and of Papa.

Tabby never heard what else she was to tell Mr. Pickels. Aunt had picked up her skirts, and hurried away.

One look at Branwell was all that Charlotte needed to know their report. His arm was high above his head in the Genii's signal of triumph.

But Aunt waited, gasping and out of breath from the gait at which she had traveled from the kitchen.

Papa announced the good news:

"The king has asked the Duke of Wellington to set up the new administration of England. The Duke of Wellington has acceded to the king's request, forming the new cabinet. The Duke of Wellington is Prime Minister of England!"

That afternoon Charlotte made out a whole new series of events for the leader of the Twelve Adventurers.

And there was the light of battle in Aunt's eye as she mounted the gig behind John Brown to make the rounds of Haworth with the missionary basket. By tea time not a pincushion or a baby's blanket remained to be sold.

It was a day of rejoicing for the family at the parsonage, as it was throughout England—that day of January in 1828.

The next morning Aunt was worn out, confined to her room with a weary headache. In the afternoon Charlotte and Emily, with the empty missionary basket swinging between them, knocked on the door of Mr. Taylor's great house set back in green shrubbery from the road. To the woman servant who answered the door Charlotte said:

"Please give Mrs. Taylor the compliments of Miss Branwell, and here is the basket for the Wesleyan Missionary Cause in Haworth."

As they turned away from the door empty-handed, Charlotte confided to Emily:

"My godmother says that the Wesleyan Cause is vulgar. She says that Haworth is part of the Lord's work which He has overlooked."

But Emily did not answer her. She was looking straight up to the low-curled clouds above them, which scudded before the wind to the black hills of the Moor.

Chapter Six

THE GENII
SMELL GUNPOWDER

FOLK were beginning to tell each other that times were better. On every hand reports were heard:

"Business is improving."

"Taxes are lower."

"The new Prime Minister has done well by the manufacturers."

But Tabby, over the smoking mutton, declared:

"Aye! Business is better. But wages are na more! Ah, 'twere best when each man spun wool in his own home, and there were na factories t' send men t' starvation and drive the wee folk and fairies from th' Bottom."

There was a strike at Mr. Sugden's mill. But Mr. Sugden found children, boys under eight years old, who would do the work at the wages he offered, and the strikers were powerless to stop him from employing them.

After that, any sudden knock at the door would make Charlotte shudder. Gaunt and hungry men were about. Many times a day they stopped to beg for food, until Tabby kept a little stack of oat-cakes ready by the kitchen door to give to the poor wretches.

Once Mr. Sugden encountered Papa on the road and paused to remonstrate about Tabby's generosity.

"Th' Holy Book says they as do na work, neither shall they eat. 'Tis the Lord's Will that such ungrateful wretches should suffer for their act o' willfulness."

Papa came home and had a long talk with Tabby in the kitchen. Tabby only said:

"If so be tha dost refuse help, there may be shot let fly to lodge in thee, as it did not long since to a parson nigh to Bradford."

The stack of oat-cakes was not removed from beside the kitchen door. But after that Papa kept pistols ready-cocked in his belt, whenever he went out walking.

On the Moor, the Genii could waft themselves away from such worries as unemployment and low wages to their own magic play of the Glasstown personages.

Their favorite hollow by Sladen Beck had been created, by them, a beautiful island. Charlotte said:

"It is Vision Island. And at night, when no mortal is near, the fairies spread their transparent wings in the moonlight."

All summer the Genii created new and absorbing characters to live on Vision Island. They called these new citizens of their kingdom the Islanders.

To Vision Island came the two sons of the Duke of Wellington, Lord Wellesley and the Marquis of Douro. Here the Genii built a palatial school, and hither flocked the children of the most royal families of Glasstown to be instructed by the Genii.

All summer the play of the Islanders continued, with the Genii's interest unabating. When autumn's last red leaf had withered to brown, the parsonage became the abode of the Islanders and the kitchen became Glasstown. Indoors the Twelve Adventurers made wild voyages and fought great battles beneath the ever-glorious standard of the superhuman Duke of Wellington.

One night Papa brought home to them some brown copy books from Keighley. On the outside cover he wrote: "All that is written in this book must be in a good, clear, legible hand."

However, Papa never knew whether what was written was legible or otherwise. These copy books became, under the editorship of Charlotte and Branwell, the *Young Men's Magazine,* "published and sold by Captain Tree, and all other booksellers in . . . Glasstown."

For hours Charlotte sat hunched over her writing desk in the warmth of the kitchen, making stories and poems in the tiniest of printed letters to fit the wee pages of the "magazine." Charlotte's writing desk was a box, shaped like a wedge, about the size of Tabby's big Bible. It was just suitable to carry about with her, with pen and ink and paper stowed away inside, ready for use.

She sat at the kitchen table, writing away. No sound of Aunt's tapping abovestairs or of Tabby close at her elbow disturbed her as, bit by bit, with her pen she opened the gateway to Vision Island, a realm far from Haworth and dull days, a place where noble persons from Glasstown walked and talked and had adventures.

Tabby by no means approved of Charlotte's occupation. She grumbled and shook her head and muttered as she went about her work in the kitchen.

One morning she broke out with:

"Have done with th' wee book! I say 'tis unnatural for the young to be so fain after larnin'."

Charlotte went on writing, pretending that she did not hear the scolding voice. It was bad of Tabby to disturb her, right at the climax of the finest story she had invented all week.

Wrathfully the woman turned away from her to go into the dining room where Emily, on hands and knees, was brushing up the carpet beneath the dining-room table.

Charlotte could still hear her angry voice:

"Tha'lt brush a hole in yon carpet. Art na done?"

There was a rattle and a bump—Emily getting up from her knees, dustpan in hand.

Emily came into the kitchen. She paid no attention to Charlotte; she crossed over to the open door to shake the dust in her pan and brush into the gray, rushing wind outside.

"Ah," she called, "here comes Ginger! I wondered where he had got to this morning."

Charlotte looked up.

On giant paws, along the Moor path, came running an immense puppy, brown and speckled white. A great sheep dog, the very newest member of the family.

Ginger rushed on huge legs across the grass, jumping eagerly at the brush in Emily's hand. His mottled silky ears flopped back against the side of his head as he leaped. His bark was deep and startlingly gruff.

"No!" Emily shook her head and pulled the brush out of reach of the big, blunt muzzle. "No, Ginger, it is not for you. But wait until I have put it away and we will go out together."

At once he dropped down, in obedience to her command. When Emily went quickly to put away the brush, Charlotte warned anxiously:

"Aunt would not like your going out. You know that there are dangerous people on the Moor."

"Branwell and Papa have gone all the way to Keighley and no one said it was dangerous."

"But you do not understand, Emily. Branwell is a lad and Papa is a man, and you are only a young lady. If you insist upon going out, do not dare go a step off the road!"

Anne looked up from the sturdy chair near the cupboard where she had been kneeling to watch the cakes on the bake stone. She added her anxious plea to Charlotte's:

"Oh, Emily dear, pray do be very, very careful!"

Emily ran off to fetch her hooded cape and warm mittens.

A moment later Emily and Ginger were bounding away together, at a romping lilt, over the Moor path.

The high cased clock in the hall ticked on. Charlotte heard Branwell and Papa come in, and the sound of the study door shutting. Branwell must be having his lessons. Every now and again his voice came to her high and excited, hardly as if it could be his lessons which he repeated with such enthusiasm.

She made a little frown at the disturbing sound. She wrote on with her long quill pen.

"From beautiful wild roses and trailing woodbine towers a magnificent palace of pure white marble, whose finely wrought pillars and majestic turrets seem the work of bright Genii and not feeble man. . . ."

Something moved behind her. Out of the corner of her eye she caught its shadow.

"Watch out! The Genii will get you!"

Two hands swept down on her long curls. Like a blue-eyed, red-haired whirlwind, Branwell was before her, eyes dancing with mischief.

"Oh," Charlotte gasped in lady-like affright. "Branwell, how did you come?"

"Oh, I came in at the back door, just to surprise you, and

make Anne jump. It was worth it to see your faces. Where's Emily, and what's Tabby doing?"

"Tabby is in the cellar and Emily on the Moor. Is there anything new in the papers?"

"There has been another robbery in Bradford. Forty stone of wool stolen. Mr. Driver told us when we went to him for the papers."

"How terrible!" Charlotte shuddered. "Why, Bradford is not more than a half-day's journey from here," she added with a wail. "Oh, dear, I knew that Emily should not have gone out on the Moor by herself!"

"Pooh! Never bother about her. She has Ginger along, has she not? Why do you suppose Papa bought such a brute of a dog, if it was not to protect us?"

"Yes, Ginger is a protection," she agreed. "And he loves Emily more than anyone. But tell me about the robbery."

There was not much more to tell. John Driver had gathered only the vaguest rumors. It was known that all the thieves had guns, and the watchman had escaped narrowly with his life.

"Papa was so upset by the news," Branwell went on, "that he could hardly walk home. And as we passed the Greenwoods' one of their pigs was in the ditch at the side of the road, and it let out such a squeal Papa nearly jumped out of his boots! He thought it was a highway robber!"

After that nothing would do but the wildest sort of play. Charlotte was the Duke of Wellington and his whole brave band of adventurers. Branwell became the pursuing villain, Captain Tree.

"Who shall I be?" Anne's voice demanded.

Charlotte hesitated, but only for an instant.

"You are Seringapatam, servant to the Duke and my own valiant companion. And we sail at noon on the good ship *Invincible*. But we are overtaken by the rogue Captain Tree in a pirate ship . . ."

"With skull and crossbones and a hundred gallant men in my crew," put in Branwell. Charlotte finished the plan for the play.

Tabby, coming up a moment later from the cellar with a leg of mutton cradled in her arms, and Papa, in spite of his absorbing study of the atrocities mentioned in the *Leeds Mercury* and the *Manchester Guardian,* heard a terrific clatter of fire-irons, as Captain Tree with his cut-throat band boarded the overturned kitchen table and rigged a sail of Tabby's third best cloth. All this—in spite of the gallant defense put up against him by the Duke's brave son, Lord Charles Wellesley, who was seconded, if feebly, by the trembling Seringapatam.

"Tha can'st lay th' table, Charlotte!"

The game was brought abruptly to an end. Charlotte stooped to gather her manuscript and pen from where they had fallen. She put them carefully away inside her writing desk, so she would be all ready at the first opportunity to go on writing the *Young Men's Magazine.*

With Anne's help she laid a clean cloth and plain white china upon the table. There were flowered plates on the dresser, but these Aunt kept for company.

Near at hand came the sound of deep barking. Ginger and Emily were returning, dirty and hungry as two adventurers upon the Moor could be. Anne rushed out from the doorway to welcome them.

"Oh, how glad I am that you are back! Quite safe, back

home, again. Such concern as we have had for you!" Charlotte
looked with dismay upon the two wind-blown figures. Emily's
cape was sodden and limp, and streaked with brown muddy
stains. Ginger's paws made big dirty marks wherever he went
on the kitchen floor.

"Emily!" Charlotte accused her. "You've not kept to the
road as I told you. You've grass on you, and leaves. You've
been through fields. Oh, Emily, if you had only known what
Branwell told us that he heard in Keighley today, you would
not have been so foolhardy!"

"I don't care what Branwell heard in Keighley. It would
make no difference to me. I am always safe on the Moor."

Emily peeled off her cape, thrusting her arms out eagerly
toward the fire. She sat down on the floor to undo the laces of
her big clogged boots.

"Leave th' boots without the door yonder!"

Tabby swooped down upon her. Her hand was on Ginger's
collar.

"Into the cellar with tha, good-for-naught hound! Let th'
muck dry on tha there, and not in my good kitchen."

Without ceremony poor Ginger was dragged off. His head
hung low over the iron spears on his collar, his feet lagged
back, but relentlessly Tabby pulled him away to the cellar.

Emily made a dash for the shed of the out-kitchen. Here she
placed her boots, in all their mucky gore, among the dry
blocks of peat-turf, and skipped back in her stocking-feet.
Hastily she pushed back the straggled locks of her hair. They
left smears of mud on her cheeks. Charlotte was waiting to
take her in charge.

"As if Aunt wouldn't know where you had been, with her

first look at you. Run, wash your hands and face, and then come back and I will brush you off properly. Hurry, now. Dinner is nearly ready."

At dinner Papa regaled Aunt with all the details of the robbery in Bradford. Aunt gasped:

"Oh, heavens, how shocking! Do not tell me more, Mr. Brontë. I can bear no more. Pray, have they found any trace of the robbers?"

Papa replied:

"None, I believe. Although Mr. Driver was of the opinion that the thieves might have sought refuge on the Moor. He said it would be no surprise to him to learn that they were lurking in this vicinity!"

"This vicinity!" It was a positive shriek from Aunt. "Heavens, how dreadful! Where is my snuffbox? Oh, that I had never

departed from the home of my girlhood, from Penzance. There is not a doubt in my mind but that one of us will surely be murdered in his bed before this dreadful time is over!" With trembling hand, Aunt applied the snuff to her nostrils.

Charlotte's hands on the edge of her chair felt icy and bloodless. She thought of all the boulders and hollows on the Moor which made good hiding places. She felt doubly glad that Emily was safely returned from her morning ramble.

By the time that dinner was over and Charlotte and the others were once more in possession of the parlor, rain had begun to patter on the windowpane.

"I will ask Tabby," Emily said, "if she will let Ginger up from the cellar now. His feet must surely be dry. I'll brush them off myself."

Tabby gave grudging consent to Ginger's release.

"Tha Aunt'll have summat to say to thee, happen th' hound's great feet muck up th' carpet in th' parlor."

But she went herself to open the door for the beast, scratching against it so eagerly to be let out. Ginger leaped into the hallway with a joyous growl. His black tongue slid on Emily's face. He lunged toward her, putting his big paws on her shoulders. They made two distressingly plain brown splotches.

Firmly Tabby dragged him kitchenward. Muttering loudly, she wiped all four paws thoroughly with her damp cloth. His big soft nose nuzzled at her shoes. He licked her broad hands with little slaps of his tongue.

"Go on, tha lazy beast! Fit for naught but a Moor hovel!"

Ginger pranced forward to the parlor.

Branwell was lighting the fire with a sulphur-tip, a long curly wood-shaving, tipped with yellow sulphur. He had taken one of the stones from the flint-box on the mantel, kept especially for the striking of sulphur-tips. He had struck it, and was kneeling to light the twigs laid beneath the peat. They must catch quickly, or he would burn his fingers.

There was a breathless moment as they all watched. Then, slowly, the smoke began to curl through the twigs, the fire to burn the peat. Branwell jerked away his hand and got up. The peat was beginning to smoke, to glow orange. The twigs beneath it fell away to coals. The peat glowed and softened and glowed again, like their own idle dreaming thoughts, as they watched it.

Charlotte got out the *Young Men's Magazine,* which she and Branwell were writing together, and began to read aloud to them:

"Four huge forms are stealing up through the garden. They have green faces and yellow eyes. They are approaching nearer, nearer . . ."

Ginger, snoring on the hearth, and the chanting of the rain outside, made monotonous accompaniment to her voice.

All afternoon it rained, through tea time and supper and on into the night when they knelt in Papa's study for their evening prayer.

Papa prayed huskily:

"Now from the coming of sudden death, O Lord, deliver us!"

Hurriedly they undressed and crept fast into bed, covering up their ears from the sound of the rain and the wailing wind.

Charlotte slept, only to dream that she was being pursued by a band of cut-throat pirates and greasy-faced woolcombers with guns in their hands. She fled before them to take refuge in a great high tower, glittering with jewels. But the pirates brought cannon. The tower trembled beneath her as she tried desperately to call for help. The pirates applied a sulphur-tip to the gunpowder.

Crash! Bang!

A terrific explosion scattered sleep into instant wakefulness. The shot had been real!

It was gray dim morning, she noticed as she leaped from her bed. Aunt was shrieking for Tabby. There was the sound of heavy steps in the corridor. Emily loomed like a specter in her long night-gown.

"What is it?" gasped Charlotte. "What's happened?"

"Pistol shots. From Papa's and Branwell's room."

"Pistol shots!" Heedless of bare feet on the icy floor, she flung open the door to the hallway. Emily was close behind her. She nearly stumbled upon Anne, wild-eyed, and frantic as herself and Aunt, like a hideous goblin, with the mass of curl-papers beneath her nightcap. Tabby trod grimly ahead to the door of Papa's room.

With one massive thrust of her arm she threw open the door. Charlotte, advancing to look over Aunt's shoulder, held her breath and covered her eyes with her hand in dread of what might be within.

Firmly she clenched her hands and opened her eyes to look. There stood Papa, in a long white night-shirt, his chin white with shaving-lather. Sitting up in bed, blinking sleepily at the intruders, was Branwell.

Papa flourished his shaving-brush indignantly at Aunt.

"My dear Miss Branwell, I must remonstrate, really, at such an intrusion."

Aunt's mouth opened and closed wordlessly, like a fish's. Tabby alone found herself equal to the occasion.

"We thought tha wast a corpse, wi' yon sound o' shot."

Papa spluttered:

"I fired those shots myself."

Feebly Aunt found her voice. Her cheeks to the end of her nose were mantled in a vivid blush. Every twisted curl-paper shook and trembled with shame upon her head.

"You. . . . Oh! Where is my snuffbox? How distressing! What a terrible moment!"

Spattering shaving-soap liberally upon the floor, Papa continued:

"For some time I have been aware of the need of protection in this house. Last evening before retiring, I loaded two horse pistols, as a precaution only. This morning upon rising, and in order that the loaded pistol might not be discharged by accident during the day, I myself opened the window, and discharged the shots. Now, madam, if you will return to your own room, I may perhaps continue my matutinal ablutions."

Tabby grunted:

"Come, Miss Branwell. There's naught to keep us here!"

But Aunt had finally collected her wits.

"I have never been so shocked in all my life. I must say that there are more untoward doings in this dreadful place than even I had dreamed of." She whirled about. "Young ladies, why do you stand here gaping? Go, quickly hide your blushes in the privacy of your own apartment."

The girls fled before her, as she retreated with all the dignity she could summon for the occasion.

Her bristling head was held high. Daintily she held up the

flowing white skirt of her night-robe as she swept on down the hall.

A few days later John Brown brought them the information that the thieves of the Bradford woolen mill had been caught. But Papa continued to wear a pistol as he went about his accustomed duties in the parish. And to keep them ready-loaded by his side at night. And to discharge them from the open window of his bedroom every morning, as regularly as dawn lighted the sky.

Chapter Seven

THE CHARITY FEAST

CHARLOTTE told Branwell sadly:

"It is over a year since my godmother's visit and I have heard not one word from her regarding my education. I am almost beginning to fear that she has forgotten about her promise to me."

"Oh, she is busy, likely enough, with other concerns. You will hear from her. Never fear."

"But supposing I should not hear?"

"Then you must stay home and learn of Aunt. Or else, who knows, perhaps Papa might decide to send you off to school? It would not cost him so very much for a girl's schooling."

However, Charlotte knew only too well the cause of the anxious lines which gathered on Aunt's forehead as she and Papa sat, going over the weekly accounts of the family. Money was scarce at the parsonage, so scarce, indeed, that Aunt had to pay board to Papa out of her own savings. The church fees which he collected as salary were insufficient to meet the expense of their daily needs.

Papa would have considered it a waste of money, at any time, to squander it on the education of a female. It was not Charlotte but Branwell whom he would send to school if he could afford it. Charlotte's only chance of being educated was through the generosity of her godmother.

125

"But I should think you would be glad not to be away *now*, at school. If you were, you would miss having your first view of Scartop Charity Day!" said Branwell.

Scartop Charity Day was the greatest day of all the year in Haworth.

It was then that all loyal Wesleyans, rich or poor, tradesmen or mill hands, were invited to a free or "charity" feast at Ponden House. Then Mr. Heaton, the owner of Ponden Mill, presided over them as a bountiful host. They came from Oldfield, from Keighley, from Oxenhope and Stanbury, and the boys and girls who were employed at Ponden Mill were kept busy all afternoon supplying tea and currant buns to hungry Wesleyan stomachs.

Branwell had always gone every year to march with the Wesleyan Sunday School in their procession from the Wesleyan chapel over the Moor to Ponden Green.

This year was to be a special event for Charlotte. For the first time she was to drive to the "charity" with Aunt and those fortunate wives of the mill owners in Haworth who had been requested to act as hostesses for the occasion. With them she was to take a place in the four-wheeled carriage which belonged to the Greenwoods and arrive in state at the doorway of the Heatons' home. She was actually to sit with Aunt at one of the long tables on Ponden Green, overlooking the Bottom, and assist her in pouring the tea.

Aunt told her:

"You are now old enough to begin to learn some of those responsibilities which will be yours as the oldest daughter of the Vicar of Haworth. The first and the most important of these is an ability to preside upon any and every occasion over a tea table."

Emily and Anne were glad that they did not have to go, to be seen and stared at by the frank and curious eyes of the jolly Haworth lasses who attended the feast. But Branwell would not have missed the fun of marching with the Sunday School for a stone-weight of Tabby's best raisin cakes!

"The Haworth band will march with us," he told them glowingly, "to keep the lads of the Sunday School in step."

"I don't need," said Emily, "to go to Scartop Charity to hear the Haworth band. Sometimes when I am far up on the Moor I listen to them practice in the Bottom—Haydn and parts of the music of Mendelssohn. That is the best way to hear them."

"Well," said Charlotte, "I shall enjoy the band, but I dread having to be in such close contact with those vulgar, dirty children who work in the mills. Why, most of them cannot even write their own names."

"You need not be concerned," Branwell retorted, "about coming in contact with the Sunday School lads. The last thing they want is to be near any of the hostesses, once the tea-drinking is over. We want to enjoy ourselves at Scartop Charity."

"But supposing that it should rain on the day of the feast. Then we would all be crowded together into the dining hall at Ponden House. It would be dreadful if it should rain."

Branwell declared:

"It could not possibly rain on Scartop Charity Day."

And it did not rain. The day of the great feast dawned brilliantly clear, a glorious clean day of early June.

From the earliest gray light of dawn Haworth was busy making preparations for the holiday. Washing and baking were done before daybreak. The first faint rays of the rising sun caught the gleam of shining white linen on the line and puffs of smoke rising from hearths above a hundred bake stones.

Beds were made and floors scrubbed in lightning haste. Not even on Scartop Charity Day would conscientious housewives allow a speck of dust to lie on the spotless stone floors.

Before the day had well started children were out in the streets dancing about in the sunlight, shouting to each other and singing aloud for joy of their rare holiday.

Shops were closed today. The forge was silent, the ringing of the anvil unheard on the morning air, or the hammering of the joiner, or the sharpening of the butcher's knife. By one accord all tradesmen had taken the day from work. Best of all, about the district of Haworth and all along the road to Keighley the great wheels of the woolen and cotton mills were stopped. Workers: men, women, and children scarcely out of babyhood, were loosed this one holiday of the whole summer from the ceaseless grind of the twelve hours a day and six days a week of weaving cloth in the unhealthy, damp warmth of the factories. Today there were fresh air and sunlight and play for them all. Today sudsboys and drawboys, overseers, woolcombers, and woolsorters, spinners and weavers were to be at liberty beneath the blue sky on the height of Ponden Green.

Christmas celebrations might be frowned upon in Haworth. Easter might be considered a heathen rite. But Scartop Charity Feast met with approval from every man, woman, and child.

Aunt and the other ladies would drive through Stanbury and across Ponden Bridge to arrive with suitable dignity on the open green of Ponden and before the tall doorway of Ponden Hall, just at tea time. The band was to start from Fleece Inn at noon, and the Sunday School was to form in procession at the top of the hill above Stanbury; the Grand March was to begin as soon as all were in order.

Charlotte told Branwell:

"I shall be looking down upon you as you march up the hill. Perhaps I may even condescend to nod to you."

"Pooh! I shall not even think of you," he answered. "I shall be enjoying myself so much! You will have to sit up stiffly at a table while I sprawl at my ease upon the grass."

Emily said:

"I shall have a better time than either of you. I am going to take Ginger up on the Moor to look for white heather."

Branwell was stopping to talk to Tabby and the girls, half-way out of the kitchen door. He had arranged to meet Tom Sugden at half-after-eleven outside John Barraclough's black-smith forge. Now it must be fully a quarter-to-twelve, but still he lingered, saying:

"I declare, what a fine day it is! Did I not say that it would be so? Ah! I surely hope that Mrs. Heaton has provided a good supply of buns. I am already hungry."

Tabby warned:

"Dinna eat too much of yon spice or tha'lt be still abed to-morrow morn!"

"What does it matter about tomorrow," answered Branwell, "when today is so fine!"

Off he started at last across the meadow. Charlotte called after him.

"Farewell, Chief Genius Branni! Mayst thou be successful in thy adventure! And bring back news of the great world to the Council of the Genii!"

With another wave of his cap, Branwell was off across the grass and through the turnstile to the roadway.

Charlotte, with gloved hands properly clasped on her lap, sat by the gate, where she could see down the street and notify Aunt at once if there were signs of the approach of the Greenwoods' carriage.

Clattering and shouting past her, up the roadway came a steady stream of Haworth folk. From every square stone house they seemed to be turning out, women in their finest bonnets, boys and girls clean-washed as for the Sabbath, and men in their best satin waistcoats.

By one impulse all faces were set up the hill toward a point whence came the unmistakable sounds of bugles, trombones, clarinets, and ophicleides, blaring and whistling to tune up for the Grand March.

Every face shone with the joyous expectation of the yearly holiday. There was a deeper ring than usual in the voices as they called out "good day" to one another.

"Good morn!"

"Good morn to thee!"

Poverty and hard times had been laid aside this day, like a worn-out garment. Privation and unemployment were the bad dreams of yesterday, or tomorrow. If cheeks were thinner and children more pale and undernourished than last year, that was a thing to be forgotten in today's merrymaking. If there were fewer old people alive and able to attend the frolic and more graves of children in Haworth churchyards—that, too, was put behind the holiday makers.

Charlotte could hear Branwell all the way up the road, as he called out ringing greetings to those whom he knew. Every weaver and merchant and shopkeeper down to the least mill hand returned his greeting, calling him by his first name, one which he never heard at home but which was always used toward him by the villagers.

"Good morn, Patrick, lad!"

"Good mornin', Patrick!"

The women, recognizing acquaintances, called with ever new magic in the thought:

" 'Tis a fine day."

"Aye, 'tis!"

They would pause for a moment to gossip together.

"How's tha lad, Judith Oldfield?"

"Ah, but poorly in bed sin' Thursday last!"

"Sad shame to miss Scartop Charity!"

" 'Tis that, but it canna be bettered!"

The clap-clop of clogs on the cobbles of the street rang like a cavalcade. Men and women alike wore clogs and paced together with long strides, fair hair blown back from their broad faces and clear blue eyes to the hills ahead, telling each to the other:

"Mark how the sun shines! Ah, but I'm fain to be alive on Scartop Charity Day!"

Suddenly came a blare and din which fairly rent the blue

sky and dimmed the noisy clogs to silence by comparison. Around the bend in the road came marching some of the proud members of the band, tuning up as they came.

There were "oh's" and "ah's" of praise in all directions as the musicians strutted past. A woman's voice called out rapturously:

"Aye! There is Will Feather with his trombone clean as a new pin and particularly clean hisself!"

Will Feather was broad as he was tall, with a white satin vest, large checked trousers, and a long black coat. In his hand he held an almost dazzling instrument, which began like a horn and proceeded to wreath itself in coil upon sparkling coil of silver tube.

Not only was there Will Feather, but Jim Feather as well with a clarinet nearly as brilliantly polished. And Will o' Ponden also with a clarinet, and John o' Ponden with the huge ophicleide which only a mighty man might blow.

Gradually the surging stream of folk grew less. By the time Mrs. Greenwood, with Mrs. Taylor and Mrs. Sugden, drew up in the carriage, there were only wide-open doors and empty houses on every side. As they climbed the road to Stanbury the street was like that of a deserted city.

But when they had driven on for perhaps ten minutes, one of the ladies leaned forward, suddenly exclaiming:

"There is the Sunday School procession on the road ahead!"

It was indeed the Sunday School, marching along with a great good will, in time to the band. The carriage, coming abreast of them, created a sudden confusion in the marching ranks. The band leader shouted an order up ahead. The entire procession moved over to the side of the road to allow the vehicle, bearing their hostesses of the day, to pass them. Cheery shouts were raised and caps waved in gay greeting. Up struck the band with all its might. With one accord voices rang out and clattering clogs kept time to the rhythm of the hymns and blaring band:

> "Thou dost conduct thy people
> Through torrents of temptation
> Nor will we fear
> While Thou art near
> The fire of tribulation.
> The world with sin and Satan
> In vain our march opposes,
> By Thee we shall
> Break through them all
> And sing the song of Moses!"

Charlotte, searching eagerly among the singers, caught sight of Branwell marching with the rest, singing quite as loud and tunelessly as red-faced Tom Sugden at his side. Looking back as the carriage swept past, she saw the procession turn and, still led by the band, swing off the cobbled road out to a short-cut across the Moor. The noise of the clogs ceased suddenly as their feet touched the heath. The tune rose clear and strong to the hills.

Mrs. Greenwood's horses trotted across a bridge over the flowing water in Ponden Clough. Then up a winding road they plodded, through a wood, and halted at last before the massive black doorway of Ponden House.

Mrs. Heaton came bustling forth at once to greet the ladies and assign each to the head of a table on the green. As Charlotte followed Aunt she noticed that the tables had been made of long boards laid across trestles, with wide benches for seats. On each table was a plate piled high with buns. The employees of Ponden Mill were busily bringing out great pots of tea in brown jugs from the house, together with baskets of oat-cakes and scones and all sorts of spice.

Without pulling off her gloves Aunt, with Charlotte seated at her right hand, began at once the business of the afternoon. Waiting hungrily on the green, there were already a large number of people who had come from all the villages around, from Oldfield and Deanfield and even from as far as Wycollar, to partake of the feast.

As fast as Aunt poured, Charlotte handed her the big mug-like cups. The mill girls carried them to the waiting guests.

A moment later came the clatter of clogs on Ponden Bridge below, and the throaty sound of many young voices singing. Falling, pushing, stumbling up the banks toward the green, came the Wesleyan Sunday School. Immediately swarms of people seemed to spring up, thirsty for tea. Charlotte's fingers began to ache from handling the heavy mugs.

Those who could find no seats at the tables found rugs spread for them, where they might sit upon the ground until the girls and the boys from Ponden Mill could supply them with cakes and cups of steaming hot tea from the tables.

The men of the band were supplied with mugs of rum as well and, to show their appreciation, they kept up a cheerful blaring accompaniment to all the noisy resonant chatter of the good Scartop Wesleyans.

Once Charlotte, looking up from her work for a moment, spied Branwell sitting on the grass, clear across the green and as far away as possible from Aunt's table.

Squire Heaton came striding out of the house to greet the ladies and Mr. Sugden. To one of the men hurrying to and fro to wait on the gathering he called:

"Here, lad, bring us rum, and hurry! I've had a monstrous morning without so much as a drop to wet my tongue."

Now there was a stir in the assemblage; it was past time for the entertainment to begin.

Squire Heaton jumped, agilely for his great bulk, onto a flat rock in the midst of the green, and held up a hand for silence. Breathlessly they waited for him to announce the events of the Charity.

"Friends, I trust you have feasted and eat your fill on tea and buns. . . ."

A shout of gratified approval answered him.

"Now," he continued, "we are about to hear players from Oldfield and singers from Stanbury and singers from Haworth. And after that . . ."

A hum of comment interrupted him momentarily. He raised his voice to a shout above the murmur.

"After that Tom Parker is going to sing for us." The hum rose to a din of eager anticipation.

"Tom Parker of Oxenhope is going to sing!"

"Him that has sung in Leeds, and Bradford!"

"What will he sing, does tha' think? Ah, there's naught to hear more lovely than the voice o' Tom Parker!"

"There he is now talking to th' Squire."

Blue-eyed and blond-haired as all the rest of Moor folk, Tom Parker seemed to be broader of shoulder and chest than any. His face, as he leaned toward Squire Heaton in earnest conversation, was bronzed to the color of autumn gold upon the hillside. The occasional fling of his head back from his shoulders seemed to say that all the world was a sparkling road to fame beneath his feet. But his eyes were merry and the line of his mouth kindly and gentle.

Tim o' Sim's, leader of the Haworth band, was rising to take charge of proceedings. Tim o' Sim's could shout louder than anyone else, so he was generally made master of ceremonies.

Charlotte noticed that Jonas Sugden and Isaac Shackleton had withdrawn from the assemblage. Such frolics as those indulged in by the Oldfield Players were not seemly for the eyes of good Wesleyan preachers.

"Th' play may now begin!" bellowed Tim o' Sim's.

The Oldfield Players came prancing into the center of the stage. There were two or three men dressed as women and one who jumped about on his hands and knees like a dog or a lion. Charlotte could not decide which he was meant to be, for the play consisted for the most part in what seemed to be a great squabble between the women, with much slapping and pulling of hair and realistic barking and roaring from the creature on the floor.

The audience rocked and roared in delight at each new slap and pinch, and when a wig was pulled off in the struggle, revealing the close-cropped head of the man beneath, they fairly rolled on the ground in merriment.

Every now and again came a hiss and a call of:

"Blasphemy!"

"This should na be allowed in a good Wesleyan gathering. Ah! Cover thine een from such wickedness!"

The good Wesleyans and particularly the members of Isaac

Shackleton's class protested the performance after every speech.

But Charlotte, screwing about to look, could not see one pair of eyes covered or closed to the gyrations on the green, not even Aunt's, for all her grim mutterings of "Disgraceful!" and "Shocking!" Listening contemptuously to the senseless dialogue of the players, she decided that there was not one half so clever at making plays as the Genii.

The Oldfield Players bowed to a burst of applause and hisses.

Tim o' Sim's stood up to announce the next feature of the afternoon's entertainment.

"We will now be honored by th' singers from Stanbury!"

The singers from Stanbury massed themselves together. Their mouths opened. They began to sing with all their might. But something was amiss. They had got the wrong key, or else they were not all singing the same tune. Charlotte could not quite make out what their difficulty was.

The audience raised their voices in a roar of disapproval. Boys called back and forth to each other across the green, whistling bars of tunes, drowning out the voices of the poor sweating singers in pandemonium.

The singers from Stanbury ducked their heads, suddenly breaking ranks. Good-humoredly the audience applauded.

Then at last Tim o' Sim's gave the order for which the Haworth men had been waiting:

"Th' Haworth Singers will now favor you."

The singers from Papa's church choir were already shuffling forward and pushing for places. John Brown, since he was thin, managed to get himself into the most prominent place among the tenors. The massive frame of old Tom Sugden appeared to reach above all but Tim o' Sim's himself. There was no doubt but that Tim o' Sim's had won leadership for himself by the length of his arm, for rumor had it that next to the blacksmith, John Barraclough, he was the tallest man in Haworth.

"We will sing," called out Tim, "an anthem entitled 'He shall be exalted.' " The beat of Tim o' Sim's arm was sure and firm. The opening notes by the bass violin gave the rhythm. At a fast swing they began the words of the anthem.

Tim o' Sim's had worked hard with his chorus. There was volume and harmony in the anthem, and sureness of time, which he had drilled into them by weeks of work.

Charlotte was fascinated by the size of John Brown's mouth. It did not seem possible that such a narrow jaw could ever open so wide, or that the teeth could ever come together again. His hair, like an over-turned hayrick, completely covered the top of his face and his forehead, which the folk of Haworth said was appropriately shaped like the round prominence of a brown tombstone.

The Haworth singers did so well that they had to sing again. Then, proudly, the singers went back to receive the congratulations of their friends.

"How dost tha' e'er knaw such a flock o' notes?" one admirer demanded loudly.

"Oh, that." The singer scratched the thatch of his hair and behind his ear, as if trying to recollect. "Well, happen it might be us going o'er th' words after choir practice at the Black Bull Inn!"

A woman laughed:

"Well, so long as tha'rt not like th' band, which stayed

after practice all night at th' Black Bull and unto Sabbath mornin'! Shamed for what they done, they took off their clog shoon and went home in their stocking feet lest the good folk hear them and know they had been reveling on Sabbath morn. But all th' way up th' main street o' Haworth they played on their instruments a hymn tune, gay as they knowed." A hearty laugh greeted the well-known tale, laughter echoing down the Bottom.

The laughter died suddenly.

Mr. Heaton was standing up to speak again. In his hand he held a large, flat, tin box. It looked like one of the baking tins which Tabby used in the kitchen.

He waved the box back and forth and all around, so everyone could see inside it. It was empty.

"Friends," he shouted. "Before continuing with this entertainment we are going to take up contributions for the Missionary Cause among the Wesleyans. Friends, do not neglect the poor heathen blacks. Mr. Greenwood and I will pass among you to collect the brass."

Slowly, and with every eye of the assemblage upon him, Mr. Heaton reached deep down into the pocket of his trousers. Slowly he drew forth his hand.

He was holding a fluttering white pound note.

There was an awed gasp and a little breathless murmur as he dropped the note, deliberately, into the tin box. He shouted:

"I have made my contribution. I will now come to you to receive yours. Mr. Greenwood, are you ready?"

Mr. Greenwood rose with a similar shallow box in his hand and in a similar public manner dropped in it a pound note.

Someone sitting at the table beside Charlotte muttered:

"They always pick out th' men middlin' o' money to take up th' brass. Folk dare na' be near wi' them watchin' th' collection."

Money began to rattle like hail into the tin boxes. The fall of many pennies meant that a whole family must do without breakfast next morning for the sake of the "heathen blacks."

Mr. Greenwood and Mr. Heaton took the tin boxes, heavy with coins, into Ponden House. They would count them tonight when the feast was over. Now they hurried back, to take their seats upon the grass. From mouth to mouth, a whisper was going:

"Now 'tis Tom Parker's turn."

"Quiet! Tom Parker is going to sing."

At Mr. Heaton's side, Tom Parker drew his knees together and sprang to his feet. Confidently he strode across the green. He turned to face the crowd with a merry nod of greeting which seemed to include every member of his audience. The sun glinted gold on his bare neck. The wind raised his hair in crisp curls about his forehead.

"What will ye have me sing?" His voice lifted to the hilltops when he put the question to them. Several voices called out eagerly:

"A ballad, Tom!"

"No. Summat of Handel's."

"Aye," several voices chorused approval. Tom asked:

"Shall I sing 'Thou shalt break them'?"

"Aye! Aye!" rose on all sides. Tom gave the signal to the band. The bass violin played the introductory strains.

With the first words a silence fell over the restless eager

group. Men took their pipes from their mouths and leaned forward, women strained to catch each note. Even the children grew suddenly quiet and watched round-eyed, as the sweet strain came from Tom's lips. Far up the fields the wind seemed to fall silent, listening.

At an upper window of Ponden House, a dark head moved. It was the head of young Robert Heaton, the squire's oldest son. In a moment he had drawn back, invisible in the shadow.

The violin smoothed away to silence. Tom Parker stopped, his voice changing suddenly from ringing resonance to clear trembling thin sweetness, and dying on the wind.

For a moment there was not a sound in the whole assemblage. Then, like the bursting of a storm along the high Moor, came the applause. It mounted in volume like the increase of a hurricane. Men leaped to their feet shouting.

"Again! Again, lad!"

Charlotte looked over the green to where Branwell sat, saw him rush across to clap Tom Parker upon the shoulders.

Tom Parker had to sing it again. There was no allowing him to stop. A second and a third time he sang the same sweet strong strains, before they accepted his plea that he could sing no more.

He sat down at last beside Mr. Heaton again, his face in his hands as if his body were very tired.

Tim o' Sim's got up to make the last announcement of the afternoon.

"And now," he called out, "every choir will please join in th' singin' o' th' 'Hallelujah' chorus."

It seemed as if every man on the green were rising and coming forward at this command. The Baptist choir and the

choirs from the churches of Deanfield and Oldfield and Stanbury, together with his own Haworth choir, ranged themselves
before Tim o' Sim's. Busily he was ordering:

"Tenor, here! Bass, here! Baritone, right before me! And
keep to th' proper part!"

The band struck up the tune. The clarinets carried the
tenor and the big bass horn gave strong and sonorous depth
to the bass and baritone section.

All together sang out the first words of the thunderous "Hallelujah."

Those who listened moved their lips to the music, as if they,
too, knew every word of the chorus. As for the singers, it
seemed as if the very spirit of the composer must be in them,
as they followed the slow swing of Tim o' Sim's arms.

"And He shall reign forever and ever!"

The women's voices joined the men's. The harmony like a
triumphal chant went over the Moor, swelling up from the
green Bottom to the dark bracken high above.

It seemed to Charlotte, as she watched, that it was not Tim
o' Sim's who conducted them nor they who sang, but a force
like the winter gale on the Moor rushing through them to raise
the "Hallelujah" high to the relentless heath, the challenge of
a hard people to the unrelenting hardness of the Moor.

The players blew and fiddled until great beads of perspiration stood out on their foreheads. Many kept time with the
swaying of their bodies. Above them all rang the sweet high
tenor of Tom Parker, clear to the rocks above, in a last, slow,
sweeping hallelujah.

In a ring of pink clouds sweeping up from the horizon,

Scartop Charity Day drew to its inevitable close. Older lads and lasses drifted off in pairs across lonely Moor trails. Mothers lifted their tired babies in their arms and started back reluctantly on the road to Haworth, with their men folk at their sides.

Sunset seemed to pile all the glory of the long day into the last brief radiance of the sky. Crimson swept to gold, almost touching the dark grass hummocks on the hilltops. Wee pink patches spread like stepping-stones across the sky to heaven; brighter and brighter they shone, until it seemed the hills themselves must take fire and burn like a guiding pillar in the wilderness for the people of God.

Mill lads, rushing along the road, paused to take breath and look and point out to one another each shining cloud, clouds which they saw most often through narrow closed factory windows.

"Ah, there ne'er was such a sunset."

Women went over each event of the day with their husbands. And on every lip was a soft word in recollection of Tom Parker's singing.

"Aye," one answered. "He did tell us that he is to go to Dublin and Glasgow to sing there. Some man in Leeds has offered him good brass. And he did na but sign a bit o' paper."

From end to end of the procession, homeward bound, spread the news. Tom Parker was to become famous. He was to go to Dublin and Glasgow. And to London, of course. He would be known throughout England for his sweet voice.

Tom Parker, eyes set to the crimson sunset above, strode as if his feet were starting already on a golden road to fame.

The women told their husbands:

"But it is heavy loss that he should be gone from us."

The glow of the sky sank gradually to purple. Slowly the afterglow came stealing upon them, with its unseen radiance near about the hills and the tips of the grass.

From far-off pastures came the mooing of cows, waiting to be milked. Sheep were bleating to be led back to their own pastures for the night. As they started the descent of the hill from Stanbury the black shapes of the factories along the Bottom came into view.

The nests of the chickens would be full of eggs, and the weeds a full day's growth ahead of the farmers. Children must be at the door of the mill before dawn tomorrow.

In the first faint light of the stars men hastened their stride, but children lingered and turned reluctantly indoors.

Charlotte was in the midst of describing the whole day to Emily and Anne when Branwell came stumbling in at the kitchen door. She rushed to meet him.

"Supper is over, but Tabby has kept some pudding for us, and bread and butter." They were set out on the kitchen table. Branwell nodded over the third mouthful.

"I don't feel hungry, somehow. I'm afraid I must be losing my appetite."

Tabby coughed and set her mouth knowingly.

"Ah, I'll warrant tha's lost tha appetite o'er too many o' th' half-baked scones tha'st eat at Ponden!"

"I did not. . . . Ah, well, what if I did eat a great many? There were lads who ate more than I and the band was splendid, though the plays were not half so good as our own." He told Charlotte: "I saw you sitting so straight and prim beside Aunt. Tell me, truly, did you envy me? Did you not wish you could have been sitting on the grass with John Brown and Tom Sugden and myself?"

The spoon in Charlotte's hand was a silver smudge to her sleepy eyes. Feeling as if her own words were part of a dream, she answered:

"Yes, I almost think I would not have minded being on the grass. The Sunday School scholars were not nearly so vulgar as I had feared. But if I had been with the rest of you, I would not have chosen a place by Tom Sugden and John Brown."

"Why not? Where could you have had a better view of the entertainment?"

"It would have been best to sit, close as I am to you now, at the feet of Tom Parker. His face was ruddy and his clothes were not those of a gentleman, but his singing made me glad that I had gone to see Scartop Charity Feast."

Chapter Eight

CHIEF GENIUS EMM I

EMILY and Anne were picking black currants from the prickly bushes at the end of the garden. It was hot, so hot that the sleeves of their dresses clung damply to their arms as they worked.

They straightened up at the sound of Branwell's voice:

"What an odd sky!"

He stood in the doorway, looking over their heads down the Bottom.

Papa, walking through the hall, paused to gaze over his son's shoulder at the murky, dirt-colored mist. It was like a long cloud settled in the valley.

"Ah, most foreboding!" His head shot forward. He muttered: "Just so did the sky appear on the fatal day of the eruption on Crow Hill, six long years ago."

They all looked with renewed interest at the heat-heavy fog and the dull glare of sunshine on the roof of the parsonage.

Charlotte was the only one who could actually remember the time of which Papa spoke. The others had been too young then to recall how rain had come down in sheets, and how they had been herded by their nurse into an old farmhouse. While they had knelt by the window watching the storm, the good farmer's wife had dried all their tiny wet shoes by her peat fire. Papa, safe at home, had watched anxiously for their return. It was not until afterward that he had heard of the eruption on Crow Hill, and about how the whole hillside had come sliding down, pouring through the valley of Ponden Clough, deep as two houses, one upon the other.

Since that day Crow Hill had been restored to summer green beauty. Upon it grass and bracken had grown again.

Crow Hill was not part of the kingdom of the Genii. It was too black and steep and treacherous under foot, during the rainy season. Only Emily climbed sometimes, in the course of her morning rambles, to the bracken patch nearly at the top of the massive hill. A giant black animal it looked, crouching on great haunches. On clear days it could be seen for miles around, looming above all the other hills. But today was not clear. It was thick and heavy.

Papa shook his head once more over the dull and ugly-looking Haworth Bottom. He went on into his study.

Emily and Anne wiped their perspiring faces and knelt down again to the task of picking the first crop of black currants. There were scarcely more than four good handfuls in the basket when they fetched it in to Tabby. Her eyes dwelt with scorn upon the picking.

" 'Tis scarce worth th' trouble to heat th' bake stone to make a mickle o' currant cake."

They left her grumbling over the basket, and getting out the batter pans ready for the bake stone. They went into the parlor, where Charlotte and Branwell had settled down to keep cool.

They were leaning, pens in their hands, over their little brown copy books. Charlotte looked up to greet Emily and Anne, explaining:

"It is far too hot to go out on the Moor today and the sun

would stew us alive, in the garden, so Branwell and I decided
it is a good chance to write our *Young Men's Magazine*."

However, the inspiration for the *Young Men's Magazine*
would not flourish on such a morning. Presently Branwell
laid down his pen and sprawled out on the horsehair sofa.
Charlotte persisted perhaps five minutes more with the effort
of writing. But at last the pen slid from her own fingers and
she too lay back. Emily and Anne lay on their stomachs on the
cool stone floor, just inside the doorway.

In the turn of the stairs the high cased clock ticked away its
sultry minutes. There came from the study the soft rhythm
of Papa's snores. Aunt's voice, reading aloud to him from
the *Leeds Mercury*, faded to a murmur, and silence.

Only Tabby, with tremendous banging and clatter, kept
busy about the kitchen. They could hear her shutting the door
of the cupboard. There was the scraping sound of a pewter
spoon against a bowl. She was stirring the batter for the currant cakes, beating in the black currants, one by one. Then,
gradually, there crept through the house the delicate and de-
licious smell of the cake, baking. And there was silence, even
in the kitchen.

Emily lay watching the copper-colored haze settle more
heavily with each ticking minute over the blue stone roofs of
the houses in Haworth below. The twittering of tiny birds
among the trees in the graveyard had stopped. A butterfly,
white, leaden-winged, clung to a stone of the garden walk.
Beneath the thorn tree Ginger's big body was stretched out,
his great head resting on his paws, without a will to move.
Not a leaf stirred. Heat seemed to roll up from the Bottom.

Tabby's voice startled her.

"Charlotte, tha must fetch th' eggs for dinner. Up at th' Sowdens."

"Oh, Tabby, not now. I will go later when it is cooler, but do not ask me to go now."

Tabby continued to hold out the rush basket toward her.

"Tha'd best look sharp to be on th' way."

Charlotte staggered to her feet as if the weight of the whole day were upon her. Emily offered: "I'll go with you."

Ginger lifted his black nose. His body moved. He almost got up. There was a twitch of his ears, a brief wave of his tail. But down again went his head on his outstretched paws. He snored once more, peacefully, beneath the thorn tree.

Charlotte and Emily set off alone, with languid steps, in the direction of the Sowdens farm.

The farmhouse of the Sowdens was the house in which, fifty years ago, had lived Parson Grimshaw, the first Wesleyan follower in Haworth. He was the terror of all evil-doers, and the firmest of friends to John Wesley himself. Oftentimes the Brontës, waiting for their eggs to be gathered for them fresh from the nests, had sat on the polished black oak settles, one on either side of the fireplace where John Wesley and Parson Grimshaw must have sat and talked far into the night about the unsaved souls in Haworth. To those black walls at the Sowdens, Grimshaw must have declaimed many a sermon fairly smelling of brimstone and the Day of Judgment for sinners.

Today Emily and Charlotte stood looking at the great wooden nails studding the door and remembering the tales they had heard about the fierce and earnest parson. Charlotte said:

"Think how many times he must have come out through this very door and leaped upon his horse and gone forth upon the Moor to whip all sinners in to church."

Emily looked up to the hazy line of hills rising beyond the grim, stone house.

"What a grand ride it must have been!"

The farmer's wife took the basket, and brought it back filled to the top with brown eggs. They were still warm from the nest.

She wiped her round face on her sleeve.

" 'Tis proper hot," was her comment. " 'Twill end on rain, afore night. Th' eggs'll cost tha tuppence!"

Charlotte gave her the money out of her black silk purse. They turned away from the dark walls of the old Grimshaw house. Behind them the gateway of the Sowdens shut with a click.

"Well," said Charlotte, "I shall be glad to get home again." Emily hesitated. Abruptly she said:

"I am going further, up the Moor." Without another word, she had turned about. Charlotte's dismayed voice followed her.

"Oh, Emily, pray be careful. Do not go too far. And turn about at once, if it begins to look like rain."

Warnings were only empty syllables to Emily on the Moor paths. The moment that her feet had started well along on the familiar turf, all the heat and the heaviness of the parsonage garden and Haworth below began to fall away from her. Gently, almost like a whisper at first, the wind blew past her ears. It pushed back the hanging locks of her hair as it did the grass and twinkling leaves of bracken moving and gleaming in the sunshine.

As she climbed up from the low fields, the wind's note rose to the sound of singing. The brown mist rushed into the hollows and left the sky white and distant. Dark blue clouds on the horizon piled in the direction of Stanbury.

She plunged on ahead with renewed energy into the freshening wind. She knelt down suddenly to spread out her hands among purple heather bells, late heather. It streaked bright among the hills, beyond, below, on every side. Emily smelled deep of it, her face among the prickly bells. She jumped up to go on.

Near at hand stood a stack of peat squares; the heath was clean and bare where they had been dug away by a sharp shovel. They were piled like a curved wall to dry in the summer heat and throughout sunny days to absorb it like a sponge. In winter the peat must give out that sunshine on the hearth stone of some farmhouse that stood on the wind-swept Moor. The glowing fuel would beat back with its warmth the eager, biting storms of the bitter months.

Emily stood high on her toes, hair flung back from her forehead, nose up, and breathing the familiar smells of the late-growing grasses. She stretched her arms high above her head, then suddenly sprawled headlong, rolling over and over into a green heath hollow.

She started up again with the cry of the wind in her own throat. It growled an answer beside her, running along the footpath. It was in her face as she went, prancing, leaping upward, her every breath the gladness of being. It pushed her running feet on through the hot-smelling fields, knee-deep in bracken and heather. Clear up until it seemed she must reach the top of the highest clump of blowing grass, and leap out with both legs before her upon the white and purple sky. She opened her mouth wide and flung out her hands to catch the moving air between her fingers. Then again she rushed on. There was no time to rest. Not now.

She must go on and on, never stopping, until she came to her own secret place.

She must go on to Ponden Crag.

She started off on a footpath which led past another farm, called the Withens. Here there were three farmhouses, one standing above the other, in three fields, on a hillside.

Over the fields the flat blades of grass surged and flowed together like the motion of a broad flowing river. Again the sound of the wind had increased. The sky was no longer white and lusterless. Turreted gray clouds were gathering faster toward Stanbury.

Emily went on, not stopping to take breath. The way before her lay straight to Ponden House. Further along, a trail turned off which led past the mill. Beyond the mill was the rough ascent to Ponden Crag.

Ponden Crag was a great overhanging rock. Beyond Ponden House it loomed, perched on the edge of a steep hill. Through the rock, piercing the granite from side to side, ran a square tunnel. No man knew who had shaped that tunnel or what tools had chipped away the smooth sides of the crevice, to square it so perfectly with the sides of the hill, dropping sheer away from it.

Emily believed that no human hand had shaped it. Only a creature of the wind and rain upon the Moor could have hewn away that rock, set there almost upon the edge of Time.

Here was Emily's own secret place. Not even the other

Genii knew that she had conquered the steep ascent to Ponden Crag, or how often she went to hide away in its square opening, with her knees hunched close against her stomach, looking out upon broad fields and hills, upon the sky, and upon the endless flow of the water of Ponden Clough.

Gradually, as she came back there time after time, she began to feel that familiar patches of bracken belonged to her. A swallow nesting in the tall grass of Crow Hill became a creature of her own. A moorhen hiding away in the bog was under her special protection.

Along a footpath far below she would watch the horses go, drawing cartloads of limestone. Often she recognized the jaunty stride of Squire Heaton going to or from Ponden Mill, or his own home in the valley. Sometimes he had a gun in his hands, and a black dog followed him. Then Emily knew that he was going to hunt grouse or partridge on the Moor.

Often, about mid-day, a lad went splashing through the clough, knee-deep in water, driving cows before him into the field. Emily recognized him too. She had seen the lad once or twice at Ponden House when she had been taken there by Aunt to pay a formal call. It was dark, slim Robert Heaton. The cows which he drove before him were his father's kine.

Emily liked to watch him lead the kine out to pasture. It seemed to her that he was fond of them and liked being with them in the fields. Once she had even seen him throw his arm about the head of one of the gentle brown beasts and lay his own dark head lovingly against hers, as they went up through the pasture together.

Emily sped on toward Ponden Crag.

She looked up. Clouds were piling thick and fast in the sky. They were dark and ugly. It was going to rain.

She hurried on. Once in the safe crevice of Ponden Crag she could sit back and laugh at the storm. From her secret shelter she could watch it with fierce, black joy. Rain and wind and storm, splendid in the valley.

Suddenly, lightning cut down the sky. Under the singing wind rolled and echoed the first peal of thunder.

Up the hill climbed Emily, her hands and knees clinging to whatever bits of bracken and heather she could reach. Clumps of grass waved like the hair of a mad woman, caught in the whir of the coming storm.

Lightning knifed the sky again. Behind her the thunder roared, reverberating from rock to rock along the Moor. A stone turned beneath her foot, flinging her breathless into a prickly thistle. Quickly she scrambled up and hurried on. She reached the top of a hill. Without pausing for breath or to glance again at the angry sky, she started off at a run over the fields. Beyond were a farmhouse, a stone wall, and a gate.

Over the fields Emily ran. Her hair twisted about her face. Her skirts whipped, like a winding thong about her knees. She reached the stone wall, and the gate, leaped across them to the footpath which lead along Ponden Clough. Across Ponden Clough, straight ahead, was Ponden Crag.

The water of the clough ran high against its banks. It gleamed black in the sudden twist of lightning, and darker in the shadow of the storm.

Emily stopped breathless, gasping, on the bank. No stones were visible in the high current. The water ran too swift and deep for her to attempt a crossing on foot.

She turned and hurried along the bank to the wall of a deserted mill. Here, high over the water, was a bridge, a plank no wider than her two hands put together.

Emily went on, holding her breath, lifting her eyes from the black, flowing current. She stepped forward, one foot on the plank. Her eyes looked beyond to the green hillside, mounting to the rock above. She ran straight across over the shaking bridge.

Rain fell in warm drops on her face as she began the last steep ascent. Stones dislodged by her feet rattled down the hill behind her. She was tired, now, in every limb. Her breath came in thumping gasps against her chest. The shelter of her secret rock was directly overhead.

A clap of thunder rang in her ears, as if the Moor were rumbling apart. A flash of lightning half blinded her. Rain came pouring down in a sudden deluge. Emily gave one last push with her heels, felt for the stone above, and flung herself into the shelter of Ponden Crag.

Rain pelted, and the wind blew to a shriek, but the stone hollow was secure against wind and rain. In the long square tunnel, she leaned forward, exultant in the sweep of the storm down the valley, herself untouched by a breath of it. Lightning darted from one peak and another and twisted straight up, touching woolly black clouds to rose color. Again all the Moor stood out in blue hills.

Rain poured in streams on either side of her shelter. Below, the flooded waters of the clough foamed and splashed. Directly in her view was the side of Crow Hill. Emily leaned as far as she dared out of her shelter to see its familiar stretch of grass, studded with rocks and wind-flattened heather. There were the dark patches she had seen last week, darker now and gleaming wet. There was the bog where the moorhen had built her nest. And each jutting brown rock she knew by count. The grass was soft and smooth, veiled in gray rain. It was lovely to look through rain at familiar things.

But suddenly the deep stream of her joy was choked and burned to an unbelieving horror.

Before her terrified eyes the bracken and the grass patches on Crow Hill were melting away.

Bracken and grass were changing places. The rocks were not in their right positions. They had tumbled forward.

Before Emily's horrified eyes, over the green grass, between the fern and the purple faced heather, out of the black heath above, a dark, muddy liquid was beginning to ooze. Like a brown and ugly slime it spread over the clean-growing things. The whole great hill seemed to be heaving and swelling downward as if some mammoth creature, imprisoned within, were striving to burst its way out.

Dry-mouthed and numb, Emily realized what was happening. Crow Hill bog was in eruption.

Over the beat of the rain and the deep rumble of thunder sounded the sucking mud, the slap-slap of wet earth moving upon itself. Slowly, but beyond any possibility of doubting that the sight could be real, the sluggish mass of the hillside was beginning to move, to pour over rocks and bushes, sliding down to the clough below.

The groan of it was so close and so like the sound of a living thing, that it seemed to Emily as if the whole black creature of Crow Hill were rising on huge haunches, as if it would rend apart the body of the Moor.

Lightning lit the ooze with a blue luster. Slowly the moving coils swept downward to the clough. Slowly the first tentacle of creeping mud reached down to slide into the clean water. A few minutes later it was splashing brown and dirty where it had foamed white before.

Sitting there in Ponden Crag, Emily saw stones and rocks come hurtling down like tiny pebbles in the soft press of the bubbling mud. Whole trees were torn loose from their soil and heaved into the stream of the moving peat. She held both hands firm against her, to keep from putting them to her ears. The sound was louder every minute. The mud was flowing faster. Lumps of earth tumbled into the clough. Long strands of grass spread out on the water, like the hair of a drowned man.

The whole hillside now was a black and slimy mass rolling toward its valley, over which Emily crouched in the crevice of a single upright stone. She tried to remember all that she had ever heard about that other bog slide of six years ago. Then brown thick slime must have flowed, just as it did now. And now, as then, it would choke up the stream and roll down over the meadows and fields below. Through the gorge of Ponden Clough it had flowed to the valley of the River Aire far down in the Bottom. Papa had said, she remembered, that the flow was eighteen feet deep, and twelve yards across.

It must be deeper and broader now. Surely the whole side of Crow Hill was melting down into Ponden Clough.

It moved on, sluggish, seething, the Moor in torment. The bog glided down making its own course the course of the clough. To Emily, watching the river of mud from above, it seemed as if the lightning itself had dimmed away in terror and that the thunder sank to a breathless silence, to give way to the coiling destruction.

She shut her eyes, and opened them, trying to look beyond the mud to the fairness of the valley below. Even there, as far as she could see, the water was copper brown, flowing past green banks on either side.

It would be a bad day for any creature living along those banks. Every living thing would be choked to death in the flow of the bog burst.

But everything must have fled out of the way. There was no sign of sheep or bird. No beast, as far as her eyes could see down the valley. No human being.

Yes. There was something. Something moving, near Ponden Woods. The figure of a man, or of a lad; it was hard to tell which from so far away. He was moving, but he was not running, not moving away from the river.

He was moving toward the river.

Emily leaned forward, arms and head out of her shelter to make out who it was that so dared advance into the face of the threatening flood. Suddenly she made out who it was, and why he dared walk into that stream.

It was the lad, Robert Heaton, and, standing beyond him knee-deep in the splashing ugly water, Emily made out the shapes of his three cows. The poor beasts were too terrified of the bursting bog to budge from where they stood. Robert Heaton, she could see, was pulling desperately at the collar of first one then another of the three unmoving creatures.

Emily leaned forward, heedless of the deluge of rain upon her shoulders. She called out, as loud as she could:

"Stop! That is not the way to make them move!"

But her voice made no sound, even in her own ears, over the moan and suck of earth beneath. Robert Heaton would never hear her calling.

He must hear her. He must, or the kine, frightened of his fierce desperation and full of their own terror, would never move until the flood came sweeping down over them. In that black suffocation they would perish! In her own lungs Emily felt the choke of that hideous death. She felt, on her own body, the rolling flow of the bog.

But the kine must not perish! They were creatures of the Moor. Their danger was hers and she must save them! She would go to them through the storm and the wind. She would run before the brown caldron of the bog to lead them out of their danger. There was not a moment to hesitate.

Emily plunged from her shelter out into the driving rain. Shielding her eyes and face as well as she could, she began swiftly to retrace her steps, scrambling down toward the bridge.

At the place where the bridge had been she stopped suddenly, looking before her in dismay. The plank over which she had run such a short time before was covered by a mud pudding of rocks and uprooted heather and dead yellow-winged butterflies. The way along Ponden Clough was utterly impassable.

Rapidly she took stock of other paths she knew that descended to the valley. There was only one that could be traveled now—a footpath, leading from above Ponden Crag, far to the right and around through Ponden farm to the woods. To reach it she must climb still further above the flood, to the top of the slippery grass and heather where rocks loosened by the rain might give way at any moment, above her.

Emily dared not hesitate; every instant of time the gruesome flood was steadily advancing down the valley. Swiftly she turned about. Steadily she set her eyes toward the hilltop and began to climb. Her feet sank in the mud as she struggled upward. Her hands grasped for solid tufts to hold her weight. It was as if she were trying to climb up the sides of a monstrous slimy fish. But inch by inch she scrambled her way upward.

She was above Ponden Crag; her hands clutched firm heather, rooted in the hilltop. She pushed with her knees and kicked her legs and over she rolled onto a flat prairie.

At once she was on her feet and off across the heath, running as fast as soggy peat would give way to her footsteps. A turn to the right, another turn, and she was at Ponden Mill.

Far to her left roared the moving mass of slime and growing and dead things. The ground trembled under her feet. Before her, along the line of blowing rushes, lightning glowed white. Retreating thunder uttered a mocking chorus to the ghastly call of the Moor.

Through the standing grain in the field sped Emily. The beating rain had torn the yellow ripened pods from their stalks to scatter them over the earth on every side. Beneath her speeding feet the green stalks themselves lay nearly prone from the driving wind and the pelting downpour of the storm.

Past Ponden House she ran without a pause. The black door was tightly closed. Sheep, in the "mistal" of the farm yard, huddled pitifully together behind their wooden shelter. Chickens had fled to their roosts. Emily drew her soaking dress about her knees, and with hair streaming and dripping ran on unheedful of shelter.

Her only thought was of three terrified cows and a frantic lad, just over the field below.

Down the road she went, through Ponden Woods. Trees bent limp beaten branches above her. Leaves slapped against her.

Out of the woods she came, suddenly, to the river of Ponden Clough. Before her, still standing in the brown trickle of the bogged-up stream, were the cows and the lad.

With three strides Emily was over the stones into mid-stream. She put both hands to her mouth and with all the breath that was left in her called:

"Stop! Do not pull so on the neck of the cow!"

At the sudden sound of a voice the lad started back, his face terrified. It was as if he had heard the call of a creature from another world. For the moment his concern for the cattle was displaced by terror at the uncanny apparition.

Emily had no time for explanations. The lives of three poor, frightened creatures, and their own lives, depended on the quick work of moments.

As she came nearer, she called again breathlessly:

"Lead the kine gently. Tell them it is important!"

With that she was up to him. Quickly and decidedly she motioned him to fall back, as she put her own arm about the big, freckled brown neck of one of the shivering, frightened beasts. She stood knee-deep in water.

The cow jerked her head and rolled her round eyes toward Emily. Emily spoke in the soft fawn-colored ear, and her voice was gentle as summer rain.

"Come, now. There is nothing to fear. See, the lad and I will take good care of thee. We will lead thee softly to thy own mistal. There will be good grass to eat and a warm place to lie down in the hay. And there the earth will not shake so beneath thy feet."

Emily's drenched arm streamed with the streaming flank of the cow, as it rested on her back. Slowly the cow turned. Then, gently as a lamb she followed the slow, persistent pull of Emily's hand on her collar.

The other cows, following their leader, fell into line. Emily guided them toward the bank with the lad following, the last of the five.

But suddenly he called out:

"There's not time to make the mistal. Look!"

He was right. Over the white stones of the clough, the brown slimy fingers of the bog burst were beginning to ooze.

They dared not drive the cows further through that treacherous silty stream. The rolling bog was nearly upon them. Desperately she glanced toward the other bank, looking for a shelter. Everywhere there seemed to be open field toward the black coiling mud. In every direction it was slowly bearing down upon them. The lad was beside her, his urgent hand on her arm.

"I know a place. Follow me!"

Into the very face of the roaring, hissing mass he turned and began to walk. Emily did not hesitate. Slowly, persistently, she turned the head of the brown cow to make her follow where the lad led, straight through the foaming river to the other bank. Up the bank and into a field.

Mooing pitifully, the kine followed the strong insistence of her voice. "Come along. 'Tis only a short step!"

Her voice fell into the inflections of Haworth folk, as if

she thought the dialect must somehow be the tongue which frightened cows understood, as if the sound of it encouraged them against their own animal fear of the monster avalanche ahead. The grass felt soft under the toes of her boots. Emily kept her eyes on the lad, and urged the kine steadily on.

He was making for a solitary hill, before which lay a field, walled in. Emily suddenly realized his plan. If they could lead the cows into that field so the hill would stand between them and the bog slide, they would be safe. The hillside would turn the oily brown torrent back to the gorge of the clough. The field would be untouched by the flowing mud.

There was not an instant to be lost; they must go faster, faster, if they were to gain that field before the bog burst had cut off their approach. It was as if they could make no progress at all lest the cows, in being made to hurry, might prove stubborn and resisting again, even to Emily's guidance.

Long brown fingers of the bog streaked dirtily through the open fields above, pouring toward them.

They urged the beasts, by voice and entreaty, step by unwilling step. The flood was gaining faster than they could go. Faster and faster brown mud trickled downward.

"Shall we run for it?" the lad shouted. "There's not a chance!"

Like a torrent of laughter the bog slid mercilessly upon them. A moment more and it might be impossible to escape, even themselves, from the sticky coils.

Then, suddenly the brown cow let out a bellow that howled defiance at the bog slide, and broke into a frantic gallop ahead of Emily, ahead of the lad. The other cows bellowed and galloped behind her.

Along the stone wall of the field leaped the lad, to open the gate into the safety of the enclosure. Already the going was thick and heavy. A pool of jelly was sucking about their ankles. Emily's heart beat heavily against her chest as she followed, her feet weighted down as if by millstones in the heavy mire.

The jaws of the frantic cows were white with foam as they struggled away. But they were ahead of Emily, nearly ahead of the lad. He was up to the gate. He was flinging it wide. Through the open gateway galloped the frantic kine.

After them dashed Emily, with the pain of no breath in her body, through the gate and into the clean, green field beyond. Behind her the lad pushed shut the gate.

They were safe.

With a jar of sudden impact the moving bog flung itself against the high hillside. But the whole Moor might have been between it and them. The kine and Robert Heaton and Emily were beyond danger. For hours it seemed they stood still, hearing the rumble grow less, the jarring impacts less frequent.

Robert Heaton said at last:

"Listen, it is going away. It has turned back into the valley of Ponden Clough." Abruptly he added: "Come into my hut yonder. We will be out of the rain there, and it is a place to rest."

Turning to follow him again, Emily saw for the first time, almost hidden against the curve of the hill and nestled within its protection, a small gray stone hut. It was no larger than Tabby's little out-kitchen and had no windows. No door hung in the wide-open doorway, but to Emily it was a friendly shelter, welcoming them.

"I've dry peat here," the lad was saying. "I cut it on the Moor myself. I'll make a fire for you to dry yourself."

Emily and Robert Heaton made their way together over the field. With the earth trembling beneath them still and the rain endlessly falling, they came together to the stone entrance of the doorway.

Wearily, gratefully, she followed him into the hut.

"I'll have the fire in a minute."

In the dimness Emily could scarcely see, but she heard the noise of a chair scraping on the floor as he passed it. Then came the sound of a flint being struck, and an orange glow. Smoking twigs in the fireplace leaped into flame beneath blocks of peat.

In the faint light Emily began to see the small space of the shelter. It was a square room, white-walled and filled with broken-down, age-old bits of furniture. A high dresser loomed forth, gray and paintless. It stretched into the black shadows of the rafters above. In one corner of the room lay a heap of old bags, of the sort that was used to carry grain to market.

The peat began to flicker in a steady glow. Emily crept close to it, crouching at the hearth, cold, shivering, exhausted. She forgot everything except the good heat warming her body.

Outside, the noise of the bog thundered like the Last Judgment, a judgment of which they had come within a hair's breadth.

Inside, Emily and the lad sat in the fire-glow too weary to speak. Only the peat hissed softly, burning.

Gradually, almost imperceptibly, the noise of the bog flow grew less. They began to hear the splash of rain distinctly against the stone roof of the hut.

It was the lad at last who spoke.

"I'm Robert Heaton. And I know you. You are Emily Brontë."

"I know you too. I've seen you in your home."

The lad's face darkened.

"That's no home of mine. This bit of a place is all I've got to myself. Down there"—with a shake of his head in the direction of Ponden—"there are too many others about, crying and pulling at my hands and telling me to put my hat straight for the church, or to meet this great man or that. Then I sit and bear the great folk or the trip to church as best I may. But once free, I make off through the fields. I come up here along with the kine to my own bit of a home."

As Robert Heaton talked, Emily lay and looked at the lights on the ceiling, smelled the warm kine in the doorway, listened to the pelting rain and the shattering flood beyond them. Something gleamed on the ceiling. Faintly she made out lights, glittering. They seemed to move eerily, grow fainter, and appear bright again. It was the shine of a pewter bowl put away on the top of the dresser. Behind it, dimmer and scarcely discernible, were the outlines of two square black tankards. They must have been discarded from the dining room at Ponden House and brought here, piece by piece, by Robert Heaton.

He said to her:

"It was a good thing for the kine that you came along to speak to the brown cow and persuade her to follow me. They would have drowned surely, if it had not been for you. It is almost . . . as if you knew their language."

"I know it, indeed!" Emily told him. "I have often spoken things to beasts which I could never say to human beings."

"What sort of things?"

Emily's eyes followed the still, faint glow of the peat. She said:

"Things that say themselves in my ears. Words that make music when they go together, like this—"

Softly, monotonously, musically her husky voice chanted. And the words of her chant were these:

> "Riches I hold in light esteem
> And Love I laugh to scorn
> And Lust of Fame was but a dream,
> That vanished with the morn:

> "And if I pray, the only prayer
> That moves my lips for me
> Is, Leave the heart that I now bear,
> And give me Liberty!

> "Yes, as my swift days near their goal
> 'Tis all that I implore
> In life and death a chainless soul,
> With courage to endure."

Robert Heaton repeated:

". . . Liberty . . . courage to endure. Ah, that's it. That's the way of life . . . here on the Moor."

After a long time Emily said:

"I think the noise of the flood has gotten less. And I believe the rain has entirely stopped!"

They ran out eager to take their bearings, Robert Heaton following Emily. At the door they both stopped, amazed.

The clouds had broken away, and the sun was shining broad and bright from a blue sky and in glistening glory on the mud-soaked field below. On the other side straight toward Haworth, the hill rose green and untouched by the brown muck. Robert Heaton had been more than right in his instinct for safety. The hill which girt about his square gray home had thrown the flood back on itself, down the valley of Ponden Clough. The kine were once more arching their necks under the blue sky, grazing placidly on the soaked grass.

By the sun Emily thought it must be about three o'clock, four hours since she had started from a hot parsonage, on a sultry morning. Without looking at her, Robert Heaton said:

"I've never shown the hut . . . to anyone else. But if ever you're weary on the Moor or want shelter, I'd not mind your coming here."

They said no more for good-by. Emily took her way as rapidly as possible back over the Moor trails toward home.

The villages around Haworth rang for weeks over the results of the new and devastating bog slide. Many farmers had lost their sheep and chickens, so suddenly had the storm come, and the terrific bog burst with it.

One lad reported that, from a high hill, he had seen kine in the field, miraculously saved when the flowing mass of silt was bogged up against a hillside.

When Papa reported the tale to Aunt, she shook her head and murmured:

"Ah, indeed? Well, the saving ways of the Lord are very strange, I am sure."

And Emily, sitting in her crevice of Ponden Crag on the blue days of early October, remembered the shuddering sight of the naked black heath on Crow Hill, and threw back her head with a breath of thankfulness to the cloudless round of the sky.

Chapter Nine

THE GENIUS OF
DESTRUCTION

EVERY Wednesday Tabby went down to the village to
bargain with the tradesmen for the week's shopping. At
Mr. Driver's, the grocer's, she ordered such staples as potatoes,
sugar and flour, and tallow candles by the dozen. At Mr.
Pickels's, great sections of ham and mutton were chosen to be
sent to the parsonage and hung up in the cool darkness of the
cellar. Milk and eggs could be purchased at the Sowdens or at
the Withens or at other farms up on the Moor, and were not
for sale in the shops of Haworth.

On such days Tabby asked a young girl from the village,
Martha Redman, to come while she was away, and do the
chores for the family. Promptly at seven o'clock, with her yellow hair neatly tied in two blond pigtails, Martha would put
in her appearance at the kitchen door.

It was one gallant morning of early May that Tabby set off
as usual, leaving Martha behind her, on hands and knees,
cleaning out the fireplace in the kitchen. It had not been
cleaned all winter and was in such a state that flakes of burning soot sometimes flew out of the chimney and over the roof.

This morning was the day when Papa and Branwell generally went together to fetch home the mail and the papers
from Keighley. But Papa had said to Branwell:

"Sir, your lessons have been execrable all week. I desire
that you shall learn chapter seven in your Latin book per-

fectly while I am gone, that you may be able to repeat it to me on my return from Keighley. Also the six problems in your arithmetic book, which you attempted unsuccessfully yesterday. Good morning, sir!"

Branwell was left to the heavy gloom of Papa's study, with his quill pen and a well of ink and the black Latin book. There was also a smaller one entitled *Arithmetic in Whole and Broken Numbers,* which was a horror to Branwell.

Languidly he flipped over the pages of the Latin book without reading. Very softly he got up and slid into the front hallway. Sounds of banging and the noise of the girls' voices came from the kitchen. They were helping Martha with the kitchen work and with the task of cleaning out the chimney. There was another bang. Emily must have dropped a dish or the coal scuttle!

Branwell pushed open the front door and strode out. Softly he shut it behind him; he started down the flagstones of the garden toward the graveyard wall beyond.

Crocuses were growing in yellow clusters at the foot of the steps. In the new sprouting grass violets were hidden away, purple, twinkling through the green. Late blue-bells shot their merry way up toward the May sunshine.

A robin, startled from its nest in the thorn tree, darted forth, a red splash of color against the sky. Another flew directly in his path. Robins were tame in the parsonage garden.

Branwell laid down his arithmetic book gently at the side of the bench beneath the thorn tree. It was the bench where Papa sat and slumbered beneath the rustling green branches on a Sabbath afternoon.

He kicked two stones out of his way, startling a chipmunk from the budding currant bushes by the wall. Aunt would be furious if she knew the chipmunks were after the currants.

He called across the wall to John Brown:

"Good morning! Did you enjoy the funeral yesterday?"

For a moment John Brown made no response. He was snipping the turf about the tall old gravestones in the churchyard, and with every snip he uttered a groan. Sympathetically Branwell watched him as he rolled his pale blue eyes, or

paused to wipe his nose on the woolly edge of his coat sleeve. From time to time, he gave forth over his work a sound like Ginger shut out of the kitchen for some offense, whining in pitiful apology from the depths of his cellar.

Branwell swung himself to the top of the stone wall of the graveyard and sat, leaning back with both arms, his heels beating a rhythm against the round stones. He questioned again:

"Did the funeral give you more rheumatism?"

"Ah, the funeral!" He held his chin so that the brown ends of his whiskers were set to trembling. His blue eyes made a pious arc toward heaven.

"Aye, lad. Mr. Carter were a man and that were a funeral!"

"Tell me about it!" Branwell urged. "Did you have tea and buns?"

"Aye, and black gloves for the ladies, and plenty for the guests to drink at th' Black Bull after the buryin'. Ah! It were powerful good whisky. I didna know where I was, nor so much as my own name after the first five noggins."

"How stupid!" Branwell objected. "How could it be a good time if you didn't even know where you were?"

But John Brown only sighed the more mournfully and cast his eyes up again.

"Ah, 'twere a blessed state, lad. I ne'er heard a word my wife spoke till mornin'."

"And what did she say this morning?"

Sadly John Brown shook his head and raised his eyes with another patient sigh to the top waving branches of the thorn tree.

"Na, that's just it, lad. She has no appreciation at all. She did fair lag into me for it! She do have a rare powerful tongue, my wife!" He sighed in dismal sort of pride at his wife's vocal agility.

"Just like Aunt. She's always scolding me about things."

"Ah," said John Brown. " 'Tis th' curse of all men, women folk! Women is a kittle, and a froward generation!"

John Brown put his shears on the flat top of a gravestone and leaned comfortably against another. He began to discourse on the subject at hand.

Branwell decided that he must store all John Brown's reasons away in his mind for future use against Charlotte, when argument grew warm among the Chief Genii.

There was a slight noise, as of someone clearing his throat, behind them. Branwell swung around.

Beneath the thorn tree, with his eyes bent on the fallen arithmetic book, stood Papa!

Papa waited until Branwell came up to him. His cheeks and nose were purple from his walk in the fresh spring air. Under each arm of the black greatcoat was a bundle, the *Leeds Mercury* and the *Manchester Guardian*. His eyes were on Branwell. Then he spoke smoothly:

"You have finished the work I gave you, most promptly!"

Branwell was not reassured by the words. There was a stabbing glance which went with them and which told more clearly than words that Papa was making sport of him.

"I . . . I couldn't." Branwell choked on the feeble excuse.

"Ah." Papa's smile stopped at the ends of his mouth. The expression of his eyes never changed. "I feared so. And now, if you will bring me your copy book, we will no doubt get at the difficulty."

With a military stride he swung about and preceded his son into the house.

Inside, the noise of Charlotte's and Anne's voices came in snatches from above. Branwell's mouth twisted to a bitter smile. They were sewing with Aunt. They never had arithmetic or Latin, because they were girls!

Automatically he began to climb the cold stone steps to his room in quest of the copy book and the pen. As slowly as he dared he walked to his own room in search of them. They were not where he had left them. He wandered into the girls' room. On a corner of the washstand lay the book, opened to the place where yesterday evening they had been drawing a map of the newly formed confederacy of all places created by the Genii on the Mountains of the Moon in Africa.

Hastily Branwell turned over the page as he gathered it up. With the sloth of a snail he crept downstairs once more to the door of Papa's study. He raised his fist and knocked on the door.

There was no answer. Again Branwell knocked. A slight rustle sounded from within, and nothing more. Papa might have gone out to see John Brown about something, or to give an order for dinner to Tabby. Perhaps if Branwell went in and appeared to be hard at work when Papa came back, there might be a faint hope of redemption from punishment.

He turned the handle of the door and pushed it open a crack. Papa's elbow was visible resting upon the edge of his chair. Faint hope died in Branwell's breast. He edged in through the crack and stood on the bare floor of the study before Papa!

The long legs were spread out like the trunks of two saplings felled crosswise on a rock. Above stretched the interminable reaches of the *Manchester Guardian*.

Branwell rested his weight first on one foot and then slid it to the other, shifting his copy book beneath the other arm. Finally he gathered enough courage to say:

"I am here, sir!"

Papa looked up uncertainly over the outspread page.

"Ah! So you are. What was it you desire?"

The icy sarcasm of Papa's glance had given place to one of preoccupied annoyance. Papa's absorption in the paper had taken his mind, for the present at least, from the enormity of his son's offenses.

Hastily Branwell asked:

"Is there bad news?"

"Unwarrantable!" Papa exploded.

Branwell sat down on the flat surface of a chair. He felt like a prisoner reprieved in sight of the gallows. Papa's fingers slapped against the article in the *Manchester Guardian*.

"Here is more talk about the Factory Act. Absurd! Nonsense!"

"The Factory Act! What is that?"

"The Factory Act is a law which has been proposed in Parliament forbidding boys under nine years of age to be employed in mills and factories."

He took a deep breath, shaking his fist at the ceiling and thundering loud enough to be heard in the graveyard outside:

"There is not an employer in the country who will not fight the passage of such a law. Ah, the Duke of Wellington will see to it that no such act can be brought forward to bankrupt the employer and to clog the wheels of industry with the exorbitant wages which men will expect for doing boys' work."

"What a good time the Sunday School boys will have!" said Branwell. "If they will not have to work in the mills they can play every day, as they do on Scartop Charity Day."

"Play!" Papa roared. "Play is an invention of the Devil. In play the naturally wicked natures of boys are permitted unlicensed freedom to assert themselves in evil."

The point of the quill pen protruded from the book upon which Branwell was sitting. It stuck him uncomfortably, but he never budged from listening, with both eyes upon Papa, until Tabby called them at last to come to dinner.

The Genii, released from dinner, ran out eagerly into the warm sunshine of the garden.

Ginger stopped sniffing for moles about the roots of the thorn tree and came lunging across the garden. He leaped upon Emily, barking, eager for a game.

"We will play school," said Charlotte. "I will be the tutor."

But Branwell said:

"Not I. I want to play about Prince Charles in the Oak Tree. It is bad enough to have lessons to do without having to play all the time about them."

"You are lazy," Charlotte told him. "You should be more ambitious. You should want to be an educated person, even if you are not one."

Branwell did not want to be told by Charlotte what he should do.

"Pooh! I cannot see that wanting to be educated has done so much for you. Your godmother has surely forgotten all about you, for all her fine promises."

For a moment she did not answer. The only sound in the garden was Ginger's deep insistent barking.

"Very well." Charlotte's voice sounded choked and far away. She turned her head from them to say: "Very well, I will play Prince Charles in the Oak Tree if you want."

Emily was made Prince Charles, since she was best at climbing trees. Branwell was Oliver Cromwell, with Anne and Charlotte as his army. Ginger was at least a hundred baying blood hounds in pursuit of the fleeing prince.

The thorn tree became the massive oak where the prince was to seek refuge and a hiding place from his fierce pursuers.

Branwell shouted. Ginger bayed and leaped about Emily's feet. The game began.

Branwell shouted louder, calling:

"I see the villain. After him, my trusty men!"

It was not so exciting as he had thought it would be. Charlotte was spoiling it. She was not entering into the play as she should. There was something about the droop of her mouth which made him feel uncomfortable inside.

It was not fair. She had no right to spoil his game. It was not his fault that she felt so sensitive about her old godmother. He would liven the game up in spite of her. He reached out to catch hold of one of Anne's long light curls.

"Hurry up, now. Don't be so slow!"

Anne started obediently forward. Branwell pulled hard. Anne shrieked:

"My head! Oh, that hurts!"

Branwell burst into roars of laughter.

"Ho! What a face you are making. It is too funny. You look

like a stupid sheep which I have scared upon the Moor."

Emily glanced at Anne. There were tears in her blue eyes. It had been a vicious pull. From Anne she looked to Branwell, fairly rolling on the ground in merriment. Then Emily pounced with the swiftness of lightning upon Branwell.

"You did it! You're cruel to hurt her so!"

"Ouch, let go my hair!"

Branwell struggled up amazed and indignant at her unexpected attack. Wildly his arms thrashed about to get at his assailant. Emily was shaking him, her eyes black and furious.

Not a word did she say, but her hold never relaxed, though Branwell had a grip on her arm which made her face white. Anne stood horror-struck by Charlotte. Charlotte shouted:

"Stop, Emily! Stop this instant! Branwell, stop!"

But neither of the two heard her.

Ginger leaped about their ankles, barking as if he would split his throat. Branwell took a step backward and tripped on a stump. Together brother and sister rolled over in the grass. Branwell's fists were waving wildly in Emily's face.

Ginger leaped headlong on the two prostrate figures. For a moment three figures seemed to be mixed up together, then Branwell was free, running as hard as he could up the garden away from Emily. Like a green arrow Emily was after him.

Without an instant's hesitation Branwell scrambled up the trunk of the thorn tree and out to the branch above. Emily was up after him, just as fast. For a moment they were both on the limb of the tree, Branwell edging out to the end of the branch, Emily after him. Branwell leaped off suddenly.

Almost in the same instant there was a splintering crash. Charlotte and Anne sprang back in horror, as the limb, with

Emily on it, swayed for a giddy moment and crashed in a shower of branches and twigs to the ground.

"Emily! Emily! Are you hurt?'" shrieked Anne.

Charlotte and Branwell stood terrified at the destruction which his leap had wrought. Then he turned and dashed back into the thick of the flying buds and twigs.

"It's all right. I'll get her out!" he was shouting.

Emily, her face like a piece of green-white lichen moss, was climbing clear of the debris.

"Are you hurt? Have you broken anything?" Charlotte poured anxious questions at her. "Oh, Emily, look, you've torn your stocking. How did you ever make such a gash?" For answer Emily pointed to the mass of splinters. Beneath the pile lay the crushed parts of the brown bench.

"Papa's bench!" groaned Anne.

Branwell drew in his breath in a whistle of dismay.

"I say, he will be furious. It's where he always sits on Sabbath afternoons."

Charlotte forgot her concern for Emily in that of the new disaster.

"Oh, dear, Emily, what damage you have done!"

There was no use scolding anyone now, for the damage was done. Well they knew that Papa's anger would be intense if he saw the broken limb.

Branwell was groveling with Ginger for the pieces of the bench. He looked up with a round leg in either hand.

"I could put this together again. It's just pulled out from the rungs."

"And we could carry off the branches," Charlotte went on. "We could clean up all the twigs . . . but . . ."

Branwell followed her glance toward the thorn tree above; from that place where the limb had broken from the trunk of the tree a startling white gash seemed fairly to shout their crime. Not even Papa in his most absent-minded moment could fail to miss it.

"It is so terribly different from the rest of the tree," Anne sighed. "So . . . sort of . . . wounded-looking!"

They shook their heads in woeful agreement.

"If we could only cover it!" said Charlotte. "Or paint it black . . . or . . . or something!"

"Like our hands!" Anne looked from Emily's and Charlotte's to her own, stained from their morning's work of carrying out soot, still black in the creases, all three pairs of them, for all their washing at the pump.

"Soot!" Charlotte jumped at the suggestion. "Why, that is the very thing! We must get it from Martha Redman in the kitchen!"

She sent Branwell, as being the most persuasive, into the kitchen to get the bucket of soot while the girls began the work of clearing away the brush.

Martha, with neat yellow braids and round blue eyes, was quite ready for the lark.

"If you'll no tell Tabby I left my work in th' kitchen," she insisted, "I'll be blithe to help ye clear away."

It was hard work, even with Martha helping. They had to go on hands and knees to clear it all away. Branches and bits of twigs were strewn all over the garden. They had all to be piled out of sight behind the wall. Martha and Branwell and Emily carried the heavy wood, while Charlotte and Anne gathered up the twigs.

At last they stood back to rest from the work. Branwell wiped the perspiration from his forehead.

"Phew! I'm glad that's done. Now for the soot! And I surely hope that the old man doesn't notice anything after all our trouble!"

"Branwell!" It was a horrified exclamation from Charlotte. "How dreadful of you to call Papa such names!"

"Pooh! I've heard John Brown call him that many a time! It's a . . . a token of respect!"

Charlotte shook her head doubtfully.

"It doesn't sound to me as if it were, or like 'honoring thy father and thy mother' according to the Ten Commandments."

"Well," Branwell heaved a long sigh and wiped a drop of perspiration from the end of his nose. "I could honor him a whole lot better if it weren't for Greek and Latin and arithmetic."

Martha, bare-legged and bare-armed, stood at the foot of the tree. Upon her broad back sat Anne, the lightest of the three girls, holding the box of soot. Emily and Branwell climbed carefully into the tree once more, to work from above. Charlotte directed:

"You missed a place there in the middle, Anne. Emily, you are not deep enough in that hole. There, now you have it. Higher up, Branwell, more to the side! That is right! Now, I think it is all covered." She stood forward for a minute scrutiny. "Yes. . . . Now you may stop!"

Down they came then, and went at once to the pump for another scrubbing.

Branwell, as he doused the ends of his hair and rubbed the

palms of his hands together, was pursued by the questions of Martha:

"An' for what cause did Emily sit upon yon tree in that manner? For she is ower slender a lass to cause all that destruction."

Branwell felt his cheeks burning beneath the cold water.

"Oh!" he flung out awkwardly. "We were having a play, about Prince Charles and the Oak Tree, you know."

He felt an uncomfortable silence around him, as Martha picked up the empty box of soot and made her way back toward the kitchen on her stout, bare legs.

The short time on the Moor before tea was shadowed by a dread of Papa's return; doubt as to whether he could fail to notice the gash, and, worse still, their attempt to cover it. Even Ginger's gambols were not so joyous as usual, as though he realized a shadow on his mistress.

"If only," said Anne, "we did not have to go back to tea, not ever."

The shadows drew inevitably to the familiar length, warning their return.

Papa had returned by the time they got back to the parsonage. They could hear him thumping about in his study as they crept upstairs. Aunt's pattens clicked down the stone steps. The door of Papa's study opened below.

Like four gray mice they fled down to take their places. Martha Redman stood like a shadow behind Aunt, a plate of fragrant muffins in her hands.

But the eyes of the brother and sisters were on Papa.

Papa's eyes were on the window.

Beyond the window were the outlines of the thorn tree!

They saw the veins swell out suddenly on his neck.

The game was up. Papa had seen the ravage.

Out of the corner of his eye Branwell saw Charlotte's hand go across her mouth, the Genii's signal for silence. Not a word of the accident, no matter what Papa should do.

Parson Brontë turned to survey his four children. The chill of a red-hot iron was in his glance. His voice was smooth and terrible with sarcasm.

"Now which of my obedient and industrious offspring has seen fit to enjoy himself by severing the branch of my finest thorn tree, and has, moreover, sought to cover his misdeed from my parental eye?"

None of them moved as his eyes swept piercingly from one to the other.

"Charlotte, was it you?"

Charlotte lowered her eyes, but made no answer.

"Emily?"

There was still no answer.

"Anne?"

The smallest girl gasped a trifle and held on to the rung of the chair before her for support. But she said no word, either.

"Branwell?"

As the smooth voice rapped it out, the glint in his eyes seemed to sink like sizzling white heat into every part of Branwell.

"Ah." Papa swept a look at all four faces again. "In the future, I should suggest that you do not place soot upon the blemishes which you have created in nature. Ah, Miss Branwell, what is in that dish before you . . . tarts?"

The culprits knew when they sat down to tea that Papa's

punishment was only deferred until a later time. And if Papa did not remember, Aunt assuredly would.

Branwell, his tea untouched, was the most miserable of all. He knew with certainty that he and he alone was responsible for the woes of the morning. That the others had not accused him, made matters no more easy.

The kitchen door closed behind Martha. Aunt began to speak:

"I hear that this Factory Act will apply to the whole of England if it is carried out, Mr. Brontë!"

Branwell could endure no more. He was on his feet.

"Papa!"

"Branwell! Sit down!" Aunt ordered icily.

But he was up now. He was talking very fast, saying:

"It was my fault, Papa, about the thorn tree! We were playing, this afternoon, and I! . . ."

"Playing!" Smoothness had forsaken Papa's voice. "Satan has indeed found work for idle hands. You may go to my study, sir."

"Yes, sir!"

Branwell pushed back his chair and started for the door.

"Branwell!"

"Yes, sir?"

"Have you completed your Latin lesson for today?"

"No, sir!"

"Is your arithmetic studied, the problems which I set you?"

"No, sir!"

"And your work for yesterday, is it complete?"

"No, sir!"

"Sir"—Papa's voice fairly rang from the gray stones of the

floor—"sir, do you know of any reason why I should not whip you to within an inch of your life?"

"No, sir!"

With his head up, and his shoulders flung back, Branwell marched from the room.

Next afternoon, Branwell lay, without the will to move, among the violets and blue-bells on the Moor. Every limb ached from Papa's thrashing. His very mind was weary with the lines upon lines of Latin he had learned, and the sizzling problems of arithmetic which Papa had shot at him, at lightning speed.

He opened weary eyes to look at Charlotte's fingers, moving over the smooth surface of the writing desk on her knees.

Suddenly he asked:

"Do you recall, Charlotte, the poem you made up about a pompous tutor?

"Of course." She looked up. "I remember. It was about Lord Charles Wellesley being homesick for his father, the Duke of Wellington, and his brother, the Marquis of Douro, and the Duke's palace on the banks of the Lusiva stream. I'll say it for you now. Close your eyes!"

In a long sing-song she began to chant:

"Of College I am tired; I wish to be at home,
 Far from the pompous tutor's voice and the hated school-boy's groan.
 I wish that I had freedom to walk about at will;
 That I no more was troubled with my Greek and slate and quill.
 I wish to see my kitten, to hear my ape rejoice,
 To listen to my nightingale's or parrot's lovely voice. . . ."

Almost in the same tone of voice, she explained:

"He left his parrot and his nightingale in the Duke's palace at Glasstown, you remember. I think it is rather nice to put in something about them, don't you?" She repeated: "Do you not think so, Branwell?"

But the "school-boy" had gone fast asleep.

Chapter Ten

CROSS-STONES

AUNT crossed her knife and spoon neatly upon her plate and raised in her long fingers a white envelope, formed of a single sheet of paper, folded and held together by a heavy black seal. The other side of it bore Aunt's name and address in a fine upright hand-writing. It was a letter that had come by the post to Keighley and had been brought to the parsonage along with the papers this morning by Branwell and Papa.

Curiously Branwell and the girls watched as Aunt broke the hard wax of the seal and unfolded the envelope, to see what could be contained in the letter written upon the inside of the sheet. With spectacles held to the bridge of her nose, her eyes glanced rapidly down the close-written lines.

She looked up finally, cleared her throat, and addressed herself to Papa.

"Mr. Brontë, you must listen to me, if you please!"

"Eh! What is that, Miss Branwell?" Reluctantly he allowed the pages of the *Leeds Intelligencer* to drop to his lap; Aunt continued:

"I have received a letter from my uncle, Mr. Fennel, who lives at Cross-Stones."

"Ah, of course!" Papa was irritated at the interruption. "No doubt it is acknowledgment of your letter of condolence upon the death of his wife. And now, if you will allow me, Miss Branwell, I have not yet completed my reading of the

Duke of Wellington's views upon the necessity of reducing expenditures of the government."

Aunt persisted:

"No, you must listen, Mr. Brontë. My relative has a matter of the utmost gravity in his communication."

"Ah, well, I will listen!" growled Papa.

Again Aunt lifted the glasses to her nose, scanning the contents of the note. She told Papa:

"My uncle describes how, since the death of his wife, the affairs of his household have been most distressingly managed, that his expenses have increased threefold. No doubt incompetent servants are taking advantage of him at every turn. Finally, Mr. Brontë, my uncle begs me to undertake . . . Mr. Brontë!"—her voice rose sharply—"Mr. Brontë, are you paying heed?"

Papa looked up guiltily from a side glance at the article in the paper.

"Ah, yes, about his household, is it not? A most pitiful state. When my dear wife died, I recollect how sadly I was put to it, until happily I thought of you, Miss Branwell, and recollected that you, a spinster, were in need of a home. . . ."

Slowly Aunt closed the letter at its creases and replaced it in its envelope.

"To be candid," Papa continued, warming up to his subject, "it has at times been a strain upon my resources. But who am I that I should close my door in the face of the friendless . . . ?"

Out jerked Aunt's brown snuffbox on its gold chain. Firmly she snuffed up a pinch of the fine grains into each nostril, with two loud and clear sniffs.

"Achew! Achew!" The lace lappets of her cap were set into violent motion. Papa choked to a startled silence. When she had recovered from the explosion to her customary poise, she remarked:

"Well, Mr. Brontë, I consider it my duty also to look after the needs of the 'friendless.' Therefore my mind is made up to take leave of you shortly and go to Cross-Stones to my uncle in his affliction."

The pages of the *Leeds Intelligencer* slipped unheeded to the floor.

Her nephew and nieces stopped eating as suddenly as if they had all been struck with a sudden paralysis. Aunt could not be serious. She would not really go off and leave them for an unknown uncle.

"But . . . but . . . my dear Miss Branwell," gasped Papa, "surely you would not . . ."

"I would do my duty, Mr. Brontë."

The watching young Brontës fairly quivered at the uprightness of Aunt, holding the letter in her hand.

Papa was looking as if he had just read a speech of the Opposition in the House of Lords in Parliament. He was breathing hard and there was a green look about his jaws.

"But . . . it is impossible! Unheard of, Miss Branwell, I protest . . . !" For the first time in their recollection, words seemed to fail Papa. Serenely Aunt pursued:

"Tabitha will look after your wants admirably, Mr. Brontë. That is, of course, in her simple fashion!"

"But . . . but the young folks!"

"Of course I shall take them with me, on my fortnight's visit to Cross-Stones!"

"Fortnight's visit . . . take the young folks. Ah, ah, assuredly, Miss Branwell. By all means, go to your uncle, my uncle-in-law. Who am I that I should refuse any sacrifice for the sake of the widower in his affliction? Go with my blessing, Miss Branwell!" Color flowed back to Papa's face, and light to his eyes!

"Go with you! Oh, Aunt!" Charlotte gasped.

"What a splendid lark!" crowed Branwell. "When shall we leave?"

"We shall leave by post coach, a week from this Wednesday."

The Genii were too excited to go on eating.

Here at last was a real adventure, a visit to Uncle John Fennel, their own mother's uncle! It was through Uncle Fennel that Mother had met Papa. It was while staying with Uncle Fennel that the two had fallen in love. In his home she and Papa had been married. Now their family was to journey by post chaise to see Uncle Fennel himself!

Papa was almost beaming as he leaned over to recapture the fallen pages of the *Leeds Intelligencer*. Aunt, raising her tea cup to her lips, put it down for one more remark to him:

"By the way, Mr. Brontë, I believe that the sum which I pay as my board to you is due upon the thirtieth of this month. I shall leave the amount in your study before I take my departure for Cross-Stones."

From that moment the whirl of preparations for the visit kept every one of them busy. Bags and boxes were packed with all available clothing. Stockings and underclothing were mended, new lace sewn on pantalets, long and tedious hours spent darning Branwell's breeches.

More than once John Brown had to borrow the gig from the Fleece Inn and drive Aunt to Keighley with one or more of the girls, for the purchase of more ribbons to replace those Emily and Anne had lost on the Moor, or a pair of gloves, or a new hat for Branwell, a wide-brimmed straw hat with a ribbon to hang down his back.

From Stanbury came the wizened village shoemaker, Jonas Craven. He trotted up the cobbled gray road from Stanbury, down again to Haworth, and arrived at the parsonage door, in one hand a black bag containing his tiny hammers, tacks, and great round-headed clog nails as well. Beneath the other arm, to Branwell's great amusement, he carried a gingham umbrella. With the hammers and nails spread about him and the children's shoes in a neat row before him, he sat cross-legged at his work upon the floor until all shoes were well repaired and ready for the journey. Then, in a leather-backed hand of the very hue of his bag, he received the sum due for his labor and went away, with the umbrella still firm beneath his arm.

Meanwhile, bit by bit, the four ferreted out information about the unknown uncle. From Aunt they heard that he had once been a Wesleyan preacher, but that now he was a full-fledged parson like Papa. It was from Aunt, too, that they heard that Uncle Fennel had been until quite lately the headmaster of a school for boys.

"Was it like the school in Oxenhope?" Branwell questioned. "You should hear Tom Sugden tell about how they all stand in line before the master there! And whenever a lad misbehaves or answers a question wrong the master throws a piece of the firewood at him. At the end of school all the lads must march up to the master's desk with their pieces of wood, and he gives them a stroke of his birch rod for each piece they have got. Tom says that once they got back at the schoolmaster. They locked him out of the schoolroom and would not let him in until he had promised them all sorts of spice and cakes."

Aunt shuddered.

"I cannot conceive of any gentleman being so treated. I am sure that Mr. Fennel has never been subjected to such indignities!"

From Tabby there was more gossip to be gleaned. Mr. and Mrs. Fennel had once stayed the night at the parsonage when Charlotte and Emily were away at Cowan Bridge School, and the others too young to care much about it.

"Ah, we did na think much o' his preaching here," she told them. "He'd not Mr. Brontë's thunder o' th' Lord. He did not once declare th' Last Judgment, nor th' everlasting torment in store for sinners."

"Why, whatever could he have had to talk about?" asked Branwell.

"Now that, I dinna recall. But tha'lt find out his manner o' speakin' soon enough. By this hour tomorrow even tha'lt have seen him for thyself. Tomorrow tha'lt be at Cross-Stones."

Early next morning came the bustle of departure.

The girls stood by, watching, as John Brown loaded their boxes into the gig. Tabby was helping him, and Branwell, but Aunt would not let the girls assist in any way.

"No lady would be seen on a public street doing manual work, or engaging in any unseemly exertion."

From her seat, directly behind John Brown, Aunt leaned over to deliver her final orders to Tabby.

"Make sure that Mr. Brontë puts on his woolen comforter to go out-of-doors. And do not allow him to neglect his meals for perusal of the *Manchester Guardian*."

At last John Brown cracked the whip, and they were off.

Curving abruptly from Oxenhope, they followed the street across the bridge and up on the other side toward the cross-roads. Here they would have to wait by the wind-swept bank at the side of the road until the post coach from Keighley should pass by.

With a flourish, John Brown reined up at the cross-roads. He got down and began leisurely to unload the boxes and pile them, at Aunt's direction, in a heap at the side of the road. Impatiently she told him:

"Hurry. The coach may arrive at any moment. It is already past time for it to be here."

But there were no signs yet of the two prancing black horses which they had seen so often outside the Hart and Hind Inn at Keighley. John Brown told them:

"Th' coach is held up, certain, by th' rain last even. A man at th' Black Bull told this morn how th' post road was clean washed out this side o' Wycollar. He came hisself by pack-horse trail ower th' Moor. Happen th' coach will na be here in any wise!"

The children stamped their feet and rubbed chilly hands together as they sat crouched within the gig for warmth.

"This is dreadful. I declare, I am quite numb already. If the coach does not come soon we will all be frozen," said Aunt.

A moment later Branwell let out a shout:

"Look! Here it comes. Look, John Brown! Look, Aunt!"

Swiftly John Brown was gathering up the luggage.

"Aye, she do be comin' at a clip!"

The girls tumbled out of the gig in a hurry as the clap trot of the horses came nearer, and the blue newly painted sides of the Royal Union post coach became visible as it bore down upon them from Keighley.

Suppose it would not stop! Supposing the driver would not see them!

Wildly Aunt signaled it with her black silk umbrella; John Brown shouted as it rattled toward them.

Then, suddenly, when it seemed the horses must surely be running by, there was a cloud of dust. Up went the horses' heads. Their hoofs slid to a halt.

The door of the coach was abruptly thrown open and a stout red-faced man jumped down over the wheel. Ceremoniously he bowed to Aunt. He was clothed in brown velvet breeches and a shining red silk coat with long tail and bright brass buttons upon it.

The man leaned over to help John Brown hoist their boxes into the coach.

"Hast a long trip afore thee!" John Brown offered.

"I have that!" growled the man. "And no sleep yesternight, havin' to feel for each place where the horses might put foot lest they stray, coach and all, into a bog hole."

When all was loaded, the man turned to place an arm beneath Aunt's and help her over the high step to the inside of the coach. Her dignity was somewhat impaired by the fact that she had to stoop far over to get through the low opening of the door. In turn the man helped each of the girls, and each, with cheeks burning in embarrassment, stumbled after Aunt to the nearest seat. They had just time to find places when the door was banged shut behind them. There was a tremendous jar and they started off. They were on their way at last.

Charlotte raised her eyes and began daringly to look about. There were two wooden seats at front and back of the coach, filled with passengers. In the center of the coach sat other passengers, back to back, upon two wide leather bands suspended from the roof. High windows at the ends let in a fair amount of light. On one of the wooden seats sat Aunt, with Emily and Anne pressed close on either side. Branwell and Charlotte sat together on one of the swaying leather bands, their backs to Aunt.

Charlotte and Branwell looked around to see what sort of companions they were going to have on their trip.

"Oh, Branwell, will you look! What a pretty bonnet that little girl is wearing. It is decorated with pink rosebuds. And see all the lace on her pantalets! There must be six rows of it, at least."

He answered scornfully:

"Pooh. I do not think much of that bonnet. It looks to me as if she had dropped a bunch of flowers on it. But see that fat lady over there. She has been winking at me ever since we got in. And, I declare, there is a soldier! A real one, in the uniform of the Halifax Militia!"

The soldier grinned back into Branwell's curious eyes.

"Good mornin', young sir. Art goin' far?"

"Good morning," Branwell answered him eagerly. "Yes, we are going as far as Halifax. We are to change coaches at Bradford."

"Well, I am going to Bradford myself, but I'll stay there, for a bit, with the militia."

Branwell leaned forward until he could nearly touch the immaculate gold braid of the young soldier's uniform.

"Tell me," he demanded. "Did you fight at the battle of Waterloo? Have you ever seen the Duke of Wellington, face to face?"

"I have not only seen the Duke but heard him speak. And I could tell thee many a tale o' him tha'd not believe."

"Try me and see! Tell me a tale of the Duke of Wellington!"

The morning flew on wings, for Branwell and Charlotte, after that. The young soldier was tireless in the tales he told. He told of how the Duke did not flutter an eyelash when the message came that Napoleon had escaped from Elba, but went on serenely dancing with the Duchess. He told of how he slept out in the open in all kinds of weather, just like any of his men. And how he ate the same food. He recited the speeches he had made to his men before they went into battle. There was no end to the tales he knew of their beloved Duke.

Almost before they could believe it, the post coach was jolting to a stop at the Hart and Hind Inn, in Bradford.

Here they took reluctant leave of their soldier friend. He told Branwell:

"Farewell, young lad. I'll take tha best wishes to th' Duke!"

Charlotte, standing beside Aunt in the innyard, watched him stride away. Branwell waved eagerly after him until he had swung off out of sight around the corner of the inn. Then, impulsively, he turned to Aunt.

"I say, Aunt, isn't he magnificent!"

Aunt glanced stonily in the direction the young man had taken. "He seems to me, dear Branwell, a most thoroughly ordinary sort of person. And now, if we can find the host of this inn he may possibly direct us to a place, unoccupied by horses, where we may be served our dinner."

By the time they reached the dining room, the rest of the mid-day guests were already at their places about the long table.

The room was lighted by a blue and red mullioned window with a scroll and coat of arms above it, and it cast blue and red patches on the snowy cloth of the table.

The ruddy inn-keeper ushered Aunt and her charges to four places together. Before each of them was a thick plate and a pewter knife and spoon. The table itself was laden with dishes: large beef pasties, potatoes and cabbage, bread and butter, and pitchers of milk and beer.

The girls sniffed with hungry appetites. Branwell's eyes glittered, anticipating the meat pasties, but the guests stood behind their chairs as if they were waiting for something.

A man in a stove-pipe hat, who had on a black coat similar to Papa's, cleared his throat. There was a sudden subsiding in the conversation. The man looked at the host; the host looked back, hesitating a moment.

"If so be, parson, as tha'd loose th' table to us . . ."

The man in the stove-pipe hat raised a thin veined hand. The heads of all bowed, as he uttered the prayer of "grace" to "loose the table" to the hungry guests.

He had barely time to finish his "amen" before there was a noisy scraping of chairs, and the guests seated themselves with a right hearty good will before the host's ample dinner.

The children seemed to have magic stomachs enlarged by the length of the cold morning's ride. Aunt kept Branwell between herself and Charlotte so that he had very little opportunity for conversation with his neighbors. The other guests chatted away quite amicably; the big pitchers of beer helped to loosen their tongues.

One large woman proclaimed between mouthfuls that she was the wife of a merchant in Leeds; a fat and sandy-haired man confessed that he was the owner of a mill, come to Bradford to try to find a market for his wool.

"And who knows?" he whined through his long nose. "Now that business is improving I may find a good market. There is said to be a demand in my line."

Another agreed:

"Ah, we've seen bad times but all will be well now. Five years ago I went to the expense of buying new machinery for my factory. I thought at the time that it was a vast expenditure of money, but now one machine does the work of ten men, and I can set children to some of them and save mightily on wages. Every day my profit increases."

The merchant's wife spluttered with her mouth full:

"Well, I canna see that th' unemployment is bettered."

"Nor wages higher," a man in a rough coat spoke up.

"Nor ever will be," another rough-looking man added, "while childer rob men o' their work, at threepence a day!"

Suddenly another clatter was added to the racket of talk. A man came rushing in with the information:

"Th' coach for Halifax is come! They are startin' t' load th' baggage!"

There was one last eager swallow of the pasty, a moment's

agonized apprehension in the innyard when Aunt was positive that all the baggage could not be aboard. She had counted only eight pieces and there should be nine. A shout came from Branwell when the missing bag was discovered, presently, hidden beneath her own voluminous skirt.

A last desperate scrambling for seats, then the bump of the coach door shutting, the slap of the reins on the black horses' backs, and off they jolted once more.

On and on they jogged and swayed and rattled. Finally the hills began to grow dim and the green to blur to their sight. Charlotte felt that she was beginning to nod. She was roused by the sound of Aunt's voice and her hand upon her shoulder.

"Wake up, Charlotte and Emily! We are at Halifax, and unpardonably late! Mr. Fennel must have been awaiting us in his carriage at least an hour."

Sleepily Charlotte stumbled up, instinctively clutching for the bag she had been holding in her lap. "Uncle Fennel? Is he to meet us? Is he here?"

Aunt was hastening off to make sure that the driver did not treat her baggage too roughly, tossing it down from the coach among the rest.

"Young man! Do you realize that my smelling salts are contained in that box? You are not punishing a Frenchman that you need be so vicious in your treatment of it. See there, you have unknotted the ropes by your carelessness."

"Elizabeth. My dear niece!"

Aunt whirled about. The villainies of the young coachman were forgotten. Charlotte's heart seemed to jump into the top part of her throat. Hurrying toward them came a white-haired thin old man.

Even in that moment of hurry Charlotte noticed that there was a twinkle in his brown eyes, and that his beard looked like fine-spun wool.

It was Uncle Fennel.

"Elizabeth, I am glad to see you!" His hands were outstretched to seize Aunt's long fingers.

He leaned over, and upon her high cheekbone implanted a resounding kiss.

Charlotte and the others exchanged stupefied glances. It was the first time they had ever heard any person call Aunt by her first name. And they would not have thought it possible that any man would have the daring to kiss her!

Uncle Fennel turned now toward the rest of them.

"But surely this family is not Maria's. This lad and these lasses grown so tall!"

Rapidly and in turn Aunt brought each of them forward for an introduction, and a curtsy. Branwell clicked both heels together and bowed from his waist.

The twinkling eyes took in each by turn in a friendly glance. He turned to Branwell.

"You will help me with the boxes, lad. I think we may load them into the carriage together, and then be on our way to Cross-Stones. My horse is cold now with waiting."

All the way, as they moved along the road to Cross-Stones, there were trees, green and tall. When at last they came to the vicarage they found it among green trees and shrubs that seemed to wave in rustling welcome.

They stumbled out of the carriage and up the stone pebbles of the walk between flower beds. Uncle Fennel threw open the door and the glow of a pink fire reached out to them. A maidservant stood shadowy upon the threshold.

With one accord they rushed forward to hold out their numb hands to the blaze. Branwell shouted:

"That feels good, Uncle. It is a much brighter fire than Tabby's."

Aunt said:

"It is wasteful, my dear Mr. Fennel, to allow your servant to heap coals in such quantities upon the grate."

The girls knelt, eagerly stretching forth their fingers. Uncle Fennel twinkled at Aunt.

"I thought it would do no harm for once to have a bright welcome at Cross-Stones; and now you will want your tea."

Tea, glowing and sweet, was a dream fluid to the nodding heads and the bodies still swaying with the habit of the jolting journey of the day.

"And now," Aunt told them, "you are to go to bed."

Off they went, just as the sun set in scattered gleams between the tree tops, Branwell to a room by himself, Charlotte and Emily together, and Anne to the corner of a big four-poster which was to be shared with Aunt.

They closed weary eyes upon their first glimpse of Cross-Stones.

Chapter Eleven

THE EXILE OF THE GENII

AUNT began to set things in order for Uncle Fennel before Charlotte was fully awake next morning. Lying in bed she could hear a great scrubbing and washing going forward, and Aunt speaking to the slip of a servant girl, who had given them tea the night before, as she would never have dared speak to Tabby.

"Such a house I have never seen. No doubt, girl, you have not scrubbed this kitchen since poor Mrs. Fennel was alive. And the fireplace! Do you never remove the ashes, may I ask?"

Between the bumps of the scrubbing brush, Charlotte could hear the girl's distressed sniffs.

"Mr. Fennel ne'er called me to account. It is na light work, and I'm ower young for it!"

"Never too young to learn the blessing of cleanliness."

There were more bumps and splashing of water. A moment later Charlotte heard her speaking to the servant again.

"When you are done with the kitchen you may start in Mr. Fennel's study. And be sure that you make fresh suds."

Charlotte rolled over to the floor, and began dressing. She glanced over to where Emily lay, with her back to her. Only the top of her dark head showed above the covers.

"Emily, wake up, Aunt's down already."

Slowly, very slowly, Emily turned over in bed and opened heavy eyes to the leafy trees at the window.

"I can't. I don't feel like it."

Charlotte, in the midst of drawing on a stocking, sat bolt upright and looked across at her sister.

"But, Emily . . . are you sick? What is the matter?"

Emily pushed back the covers and sat up.

"No, I'm not sick. It's those trees!"

Charlotte turned startled eyes to the window.

It was like a green forest compared to the bare heath of the Moor. Poplars and giant elms spread shade over the grass. Green branches twinkled in the early sunlight.

"Whatever," asked Charlotte in amazement, "is wrong with the trees? I think they are lovely. Oh, it's all so much prettier than things are at home. Look at the nice yellow flowers in the garden. They're bigger and brighter than any we've got."

"That's just it!" said Emily. "It's all so prim and fine and regular, it's like something pressing against me. I want to be back in our bracken and our heather. I can't breathe here!"

Both hands went suddenly to her chest as if there were really something there, weighing her down.

Charlotte knelt to her stocking again, still puzzled.

"Well, if it's nothing really wrong," she said briefly, "you'd better hurry and dress or Aunt will come and rout you out."

She brushed her hair hurriedly. Emily, with a long gasping sigh, flung herself from bed at last. With another hasty brush, Charlotte stood at the door.

"I'm going out now," she called back. "I am all ready and I don't want to miss anything. I rather like being at Cross-Stones."

There were certainly many new things to see. They spent all morning beneath the trees in the meadow and in the garden with Uncle Fennel, while Aunt kept the poor servant busy as a beaver about the house with the washing and the scrubbing.

They came in to dinner by way of the schoolroom. It was a cheerful, light room, Charlotte noticed. There were two rows of desks and a shelfful of books, books of French and

history. A map hung on the wall. Strewn over the desks were Greek and Latin books like those which Branwell had to read with Papa.

At dinner Uncle Fennel suggested to Aunt:

"Since the children are staying for a fortnight, why could they not have their daily lessons with me? That will leave you free of all responsibilities, beyond those you have already undertaken in my behalf."

Aunt agreed at once.

"My duty is plainly to continue entirely with this house. Such a condition as it is in, Mr. Fennel! And such a servant is unbelievable! I have been sent by the Lord to give you a thorough house-cleaning!"

So it was arranged that the empty schoolroom should be used by Uncle Fennel and his new pupils. While every other part of the house was scrubbed and cleaned from end to end under the stern eye of Aunt, Uncle Fennel read aloud with them from the history books. It was Uncle Fennel who gave Charlotte her first lesson in French, and Branwell his first in drawing.

Once, during a dull hour when Uncle Fennel was reading aloud to them in a sweet and sonorous voice, Branwell drew toward himself Uncle Fennel's own copy of Ferguson's *Roman Republic*. He proceeded to sketch on its margins Uncle Fennel's head in the light of the window, with the trees in the shadow behind it. Then, grinning at his own impudence, he gave Charlotte a kick and passed his masterpiece across the aisle to her.

"What have you there, lad?"

John Fennel had not been twelve years headmaster of a

boys' school for nothing. To the horror of Charlotte he reached out a hand for the book. With crimson cheeks Charlotte passed it to him.

For a moment Uncle Fennel examined it. Then, to the utter surprise of them all, he laughed. He gave the book back with twinkling eyes.

"You've a talent there, lad, but you need a lesson or two. We'll try to see what you can do from nature."

It was hard to believe that Uncle Fennel was a real schoolmaster, like poor Mr. Patchett of Oxenhope. His teaching was so pleasant that lessons were a joy to them all. Only once did they see him really angry, and then it was not on their account.

One morning, just as they had finished their geography, a little boy dressed in the familiar apron worn by the mill hands came knocking at the door of the schoolroom. He wanted to know where he might deliver a parcel, some worsted goods which Aunt had ordered for the house.

At first Charlotte did not think Uncle Fennel was going to answer the lad. When he did speak, it was to ask a question, himself.

"Do you work all day in the mills?"

The grimy-faced lad nodded.

"Aye! I'm sudsboy!"

"What hours do you work?"

The lad, who was a full head shorter than Anne, answered timidly: "Six in th' morning, till eight at night, please, yer honor."

"And your father takes all your wages?"

"Aye, certain!" The lad answered in puzzled suprise.

When Uncle Fennel had re-directed the lad to Aunt, he turned back to the schoolroom still frowning.

"Ah, the pity of it! Such a lad should be in school or out in the fields in the sunshine, not having the life and youth choked out of him by the hot closeness of a worsted mill. The day is not far off when there will be a law against such conditions."

Branwell spoke up:

"You mean the Factory Act, do you not? Papa has read us about it, from the *Manchester Guardian*."

"Papa says," put in Charlotte, "that every employer in the country will protest against such a law being passed."

Uncle Fennel's eyes seemed to be seeing clean through the wall behind them. His voice was more stern than they had ever heard it:

"Yes, many will protest, and many will fight. It means money in the pockets of the employers to have lads like this one, who will work for practically nothing. Money and ease for themselves, while grown men are starving for lack of work. I tell you it is the souls of such employers that will be required of them in the Day of Judgment!"

Anne looked up startled. It was the first mention that Uncle Fennel had made of souls and the Judgment. But the Judgment of which he spoke had nothing to do with disobedient or careless little girls, and she was not frightened of his eyes. Now they were growing gentle again, and his voice was ringing deep as he said:

"Perhaps it is only the dream of an old man. But I believe that some day, not too far away, there will not be a lad in England to whom youth will be denied."

After the incident of the drawing Branwell went out with Uncle Fennel with his pencil and paper and sat for hours sketching a tree or a point of rock. At first Charlotte went out with them, but there were so many leaves to sketch! And the wind would not let the leaves stay still long enough for her to copy them, so Uncle Fennel brought out two prints of his own and set Charlotte and Emily to copying them line for line in the schoolroom, while Branwell went on sketching from nature in the sunlit garden.

He even went so far, one morning, as to get up early and slide out to his favorite spot in the garden, to catch the sunlight slanting just right over the particular edge of wall in which he was interested. Charlotte and Anne went out to call him in for breakfast. Charlotte told him:

"Why, Branwell, you have never worked so hard at anything in all your life before!"

"No!" he agreed. "There has never been anything before worth the trouble. But I say, Charlotte, it is maddening, you know, when a tree is blowing like a hurricane and then the moment I try to put it on paper it simply won't look as if it were moving!"

"How can it move," asked Charlotte, "when it is on paper?"

"It seems to me," said Anne, "that things here at Cross-Stones are just opposite to the way they are at home. There Branwell is always the last down and Emily the first. But now for three mornings Emily has been late for breakfast! Oh, dear! There is Uncle calling, and she will be late again!"

As they came in, there was a heavy plod of feet on the stairs; Emily, walking as if she could scarcely drag one foot after the other, trailed behind them into the breakfast room.

Charlotte, glancing up as she unfolded her napkin on her lap, noticed worriedly that there were great brown circles about her eyes as if she had not slept for a week.

Uncle Fennel must have noticed it, too, for he suddenly broke into Aunt's good-morning speech, saying:

"I think, if you have no objections, Elizabeth, that I shall take Branwell and the girls on a picnic today, to Kirkstall Abbey. It is not far, and it is a pleasant sunny day for a drive."

Directly breakfast was over they ran up to put on their pelisses and bonnets, to be ready by the time Uncle Fennel should have harnessed his gray horse to the carriage. As they started off, the sun twinkled a cheery greeting through the trees. Even Emily seemed to be brighter, and less pitifully tired and heavy eyed, as the good earthy smells of early autumn came to them.

They saw great ruined stone houses, like castles. Behind and about them on every side, rolling farmlands and small, many-gabled houses. They saw carved-in coats of arms, stone shields, and crossed stone swords, beaten by rain and wind but still standing bravely in the ruins of high stone walls. Charlotte felt a tingling beneath her skin, as if she had ventured suddenly a hundred or more years into the past. She decided that Branwell must draw such a coat of arms for the Twelve Adventurers, a crimson sun on a white field, with the Genii's call of victory beneath it in flaming letters.

The curving road took them through the village of Hartshead. Uncle Fennel pointed out a house on the right. It was a neat white house with green fresh paint upon the door and window sills. There was a wide lawn before it, and between the tall trees they could catch bright glimpses of a garden.

"In that house," said Uncle Fennel, "lives a lady you must all know well, she was so great a friend to your father and mother. That is the home of Mrs. Thomas Atkinson."

"Mrs. Thomas Atkinson!" Charlotte echoed his words. "Is that indeed my godmother's house? Oh, stop, please, Uncle, that I may see it more closely. Why, I had no idea that my godmother lived so close to Cross-Stones."

There were heavy curtains at the windows, so that they could not see in; they peered over the gate to look into the garden.

"How tidy it is!" said Anne. "See how all the flowers are in rows."

"Look!" Branwell pointed. "I do believe that there is a fountain playing. It is, indeed. Look there, Charlotte. Is that not elegant?"

But Charlotte said only:

"My godmother must have laughed at our ugly garden, just as she did at my clothing. I do not wonder that she never bothered about her promise to me."

"And what was the promise," Uncle Fennel asked, "which your godmother made to you?"

Branwell answered for her:

"Oh, Mrs. Atkinson promised Charlotte, you know, that she would help her with her education."

Uncle Fennel turned again toward Charlotte.

"And do you not think," he asked, "that your godmother will keep her word to you?"

Charlotte answered him:

"I am afraid not. I have never heard from her since the day she visited me."

She could not be long downcast with so joyous a companion at her side as Uncle Fennel, and she was soon lost once more in pleasure of the green woodland and the soft morning mist slanting between the trees.

Presently, as they passed over a bridge and a soft gurgling wide stream, the sound of voices startled them.

They were girls' voices, high-pitched, and interspersed with laughter. In a moment they rounded another curve and saw the girls themselves walking along the road. There were about eight of them, all of different ages, trim and neat looking. At their head, almost like one of the girls herself, walked an older woman, with rosy cheeks, her hair braided in a soft brown coronet about her forehead.

The girls drew to the side of the road to let the carriage pass. But Uncle Fennel, as they trotted by, almost stood in his place to make a sweeping bow to the brown-haired lady. She smiled warmly and bowed in return, while the girls all bobbed curtsies.

Branwell leaned forward in frank curiosity to look at them. Charlotte shrank back as far as she could beside Uncle Fennel, with both eyes wide open to take in every detail of the party. Emily and Anne had quite disappeared into the shadowy recesses of the carriage.

The horse swung around another bend, hiding the laughing group from sight. Immediately Charlotte inquired of Uncle Fennel.

"Who was that pretty lady? And are all those girls her daughters?"

Uncle Fennel laughed, leaning forward to give the whip to the slow-trotting horse.

"Daughters! Now that is a poor guess! That was Miss Wooler. She is mistress of a school for young ladies, called Roehead. We shall see it presently, since it lies directly in our route today."

They emerged in a moment on the Leeds-to-Huddersfield road and had gone a little way when Uncle Fennel reined in the horses before what appeared to be an empty field. With the end of his whip he pointed.

"There is Roehead! That large house at the end of the field. It is a fine house, you see, with two tiers of bowed windows, and plenty of light by which the girls may study."

Charlotte remembered the few tiny windows at Cowan Bridge and looked with amazement and admiration at the big rambling house nearly hidden from the road, the sun gleaming like gold on its huge windows. With a clutch of envy that was almost like a pain, she thought of the laughing round-cheeked girls. What things they must do together in that big house with that pleasant Miss Wooler! There must surely be a room behind that highest window where they all could study together with light flooding in on them, and the dormitory where they would whisper stories far into the night.

She told Uncle Fennel eagerly:

"But they didn't look one bit like a boarding school, those girls! At Cowan Bridge we would always go in order two and two like a procession, when we went for a walk!"

Uncle Fennel shook his head.

"Miss Wooler does not believe in such strict discipline for the girls at Roehead. And they are a happy, healthy group, as you have seen. But come, we must get on to our picnic. Come along, Waterloo!" Waterloo, the gray horse, trotted off.

They turned now into the way which led to the ruins of Kirkstall Abbey, through the thick leafy glades of Kirklees Park. Here in every direction were thick woods with foliage so dense that the sunlight struggled through only in patches.

Finally Uncle Fennel reined in the horse at the side of the road. They dismounted from their carriage and started off over the velvet smoothness of the turf, Branwell hugging the picnic basket.

Anne said:

"Emily, listen to the strange noise the wind makes. Do you hear it?"

"Yes!" Emily answered below her breath. "I have heard it ever since we came to Cross-Stones. The tune of it makes my throat ache."

Wind, rustling through the leaves, was a strange song to Emily. The song of the Moor was the steady high-pitched drone of wind through grass.

They came at last to the gray stones of Kirkstall Abbey. Here Charlotte spread out the lunch among the moss-grown ruins.

As they sat under the trees Uncle Fennel told them the story of Robin Hood, the most beloved rogue in all merry England, who had died here hundreds of years ago and had been buried, as he asked that he might be, beneath the trees of the green wood.

"They say," finished the story-teller, "that his presence still haunts the woods and that he and his men still hunt with their long bows in the shadowy light."

Emily listened with her eyes upon the distant sunlit patches as if she could make out the wild shadowy spirit of the outlaw.

She touched not a morsel of the picnic lunch, though Branwell ate like a starving man, and the others were not far behind in appetite.

At last Charlotte shook the crumbs from the bottom of the basket and the group made its way slowly back again on noiseless feet, like Robin Hood himself, through the multitude of black tree trunks to the road.

By the bank, Waterloo was patiently waiting. Eagerly she nibbled the piece of sugar which Branwell had saved from the lunch for her, before they mounted once more into the carriage.

As they started home, Uncle Fennel turned, with the reins held loosely in his hands, to look with a sadder smile than usual into Charlotte's brown eyes.

"Do you know, my dear," he told her with a sort of a croak in his voice, "I used to sit, just so, beside your mother when she was not much older than you, and hardly larger? And we would come together on picnics to this very spot."

"My mother!" Charlotte thought of the lettering on the tablet in Haworth Church:

"Maria Brontë, Wife of the Reverend P. Brontë, A.B., Minister of Haworth. Her soul departed to the Saviour, September 15th, 1821."

All she could remember now of that small pale mother was a pair of cool white hands on a little girl's hot cheeks, the sweet-faced woman holding little Branwell on her knee. There was a presence for Charlotte in the green wood of Kirklees Park gentler than that of the high-hearted Robin Hood, and a shadow more serene than the clear pattern of the leaves on the grass by the roadside.

That was their last outing. The very next morning they woke to the patter of rain on the roof, and to the sight of it dripping from leaf to glossy leaf of the trees as it streaked down the windowpanes.

They worked at their lessons all morning. In the afternoon Charlotte shut herself up in Uncle Fennel's big library. She had a guilty feeling that Aunt might be searching for her to help in the house-cleaning. She had seen Walter Scott's name among the titles of the books a few days before. Now, if she kept very quiet, perhaps Aunt might not be reminded of her.

Kneeling before the great bookcase she ran her eyes over the titles. Ah, there was the *History of the Emperor Napoleon!* That was sure to have something in it about the Duke of Wellington.

Charlotte took the big volume beneath her arm and scurried for the nearest armchair. Quickly she turned over the pages; she read like a hungry man attacking a piece of bread by tearing it off in chunks. Hardly had she devoured one page before she started in desperate haste on the next, turning page after page with the most unbelievable rapidity. Greedily she read:

"The character of the Duke of Wellington is one of the most wonderful that ever man had . . . his mind approaches as nearly to the perfection of greatness as human fallibility will allow. . . ."

The sound of the rain went on monotonously, but Charlotte would not have heard the wildest storm beating at the window of Uncle Fennel's library.

Slowly but surely Uncle Fennel's house was being set in order. Aunt dismissed the young maid, and got an older woman with broad face and iron-gray hair, who would do the work.

She ordered Charlotte to write to Papa to say that they would return the following Wednesday to Haworth.

So once more they packed up boxes and stuffed carpetbags, and set out in the carriage with Uncle Fennel.

"By next year," he told them as he jogged along, "there will be a new way to travel in England. They are now at work on a railway for passenger traffic between Liverpool and Manchester."

"For passenger traffic!" Aunt was horrified. "But such a thing is inconceivable. I should certainly never risk *my* life by such a dangerous mode of travel. Nor will any man with consideration for his life. It is a well-known fact that if the pace of ten or twelve miles an hour is exceeded it becomes impossible to breathe!"

Once more in the innyard, Uncle Fennel kissed Aunt.

"Good-by, Elizabeth, my dear. And tell Mr. Brontë that I am expecting a visit from him very soon, before the cold weather has set in."

He kissed the girls and gave Branwell his hand. They were off.

The Brontës made the return journey by post coach as they had come. About evening they were set down at the cross-roads.

And who should come down in the gig to meet them at the cross-roads but Papa himself.

"It occurred to me," he told Aunt, "that the evening air would benefit my health." He had even remembered to bring a warm blanket for their feet.

They rattled over the familiar cobbles once more, up the last hill to the single house at the top of the street. There in the glow of the parsonage doorway stood Tabby. She greeted them sourly:

"Well, th' tea's high boilt off, waitin' on ye. Tha'st good rosy cheeks, Branwell! But Emily looks peaked, certain!"

Emily turned to look down the road over the blue twilight in the valley. In the bustle of getting the boxes to their various rooms she slipped away from the others.

As Charlotte and Anne were making hurried preparations for tea, Branwell appeared in the doorway of their room.

"What do you suppose John Brown told me?" he informed them excitedly. "Tom Parker is back in Haworth. He sang in Glasgow and he was a great success. But one night, in the very middle of a concert, he stopped singing. He walked right out of the theater before all the audience. And he took the next post coach for home."

"Why ever," gasped Charlotte, "did he do that?"

"John Brown says that he told folk here that it was home-sickness! It made him feel so terrible that he could not sing another note for wanting to be back on the Moor, and away from cities and big towns."

A moment later Emily came in. It seemed to Charlotte that she could see a shade of pink in her cheeks. Certainly there was a fresh light in her eyes as she told them:

"I've been out on the Moor again. Just a little way, but far enough to hear the song in the grass."

Charlotte said suddenly:

"Emily! I know what was the trouble with you at Cross-Stones! It was *homesickness!*"

Emily began to change her dress with rapid fingers in the chilly dark-lit room. With strong arms she brushed out her dark straight hair and flung it back over her shoulders. On both feet she stood, like a piece of ling heather which had got its root once more, safe and fast in the peat.

Chapter Twelve

THE FAREWELL OF THE
GENII

AUTUMN 1830. As long as the snow held back and the Moor was dry, the Genii went out on it to play. The becks were frosted with thin ice and the children's feet and arms were so numb that they dared not sit still for a minute on the hard, frozen ground. Races and battles and plays kept going full tilt on the hard black heath. They pounded up and down over the hills, with faces burning in the wind. And then came home to tea at last with shockingly red cheeks and noses, hair unkempt, and hands raw and chapped.

"In that bitter wind!" Aunt drew her black silk closer about the bones of her shoulder blades. "One would think you were all young animals, instead of little ladies!"

Tabby, though she scolded them roundly for the dirt and dried grass which streaked the kitchen floor, found plenty of excuse for them before Aunt.

"They are na so old," she maintained, "but they may frolic on th' Moor."

Papa said: "I do not believe it will hurt them, my dear Miss Branwell. Many a time I have walked over winter moors with not even a coat upon my back."

So they were left to seek their own adventure between the parsonage and the Moor. Charlotte planned the plays for the Twelve Adventurers and the Islanders on the Moor by day. In the evening, by the grate in the parlor, Charlotte and Branwell brought out brown copy books and wrote their *Young Men's Magazine* and *Tales of the Islanders*.

Sometimes discussion ran high. Branwell objected:

"There is far too much love-making. I do not care if the Marquis of Douro is betrothed to Lady Marian Hume. That is not reason enough why he should rave about her portrait or the moon and the stars."

"Well, then, what if the wicked and glamorous Lady Zenobia Ellrington gives him her portrait? Oh, yes, that is it. And he shall ask a curl of her long black tresses in return!"

Branwell groaned:

"But that is not a real adventure. I mean something like the Duke of Wellington conquering the savage Ashantis; and Captain Tree absconding with the money of his fair young ward, or Sergeant Bud attempting to assault the Marquis of Douro in the dead of night with the help of four of his lusty brigands."

"And I wish"—Anne shivered suddenly—"that there were not quite so much about ghosts in some of the stories, or deaths and buryings and things like that."

Furiously Charlotte turned on them.

"Well! That shows how little any of you appreciate true genius. Any real author makes use of romance and the supernatural over and over again. There is not a single good novel written without sentiment and mystery. As if it were not hard enough to be any sort of an author, in such a dull place as Haworth!"

Emily demanded in amazement:

"Why, whatever is wrong with it here? And now is the best

time of year, when the sky is always purple and gray, and your face tingles with the wind."

Charlotte told her bitterly:

"You don't understand. You don't know what it is to have genius burning within you. To write and write, and all the time to know that your writings will never be appreciated as they should be, that the world will never read them."

"I should hate to have the world read my writings," said Emily. "I hope that *I* shall never be famous."

"Never worry," Branwell told her. "You may be sure that no one from Haworth will ever become famous."

Charlotte watched through a blur of tears her own fingers moving on her manuscript, putting the passionate hopelessness within her into words of poetry. Furiously she wrote:

> None can tell the bitter anguish
> Of those lofty souls that languish
>   With grim penury still dwelling:
> Quenched by frown their sacred fire,
>   All their powers within them swelling
> Tortured by neglect to ire. . . .

The tears dried on her cheeks. Even in the writing there was consolation. There was magic, still in *making out*.

Next morning Charlotte opened her eyes on a gray day, clouds scudding low against the blackened heather on the hills.

She stretched out her fingers to the place where Emily should be. But Emily was gone already up the Moor, to make the best of the few days left before the winter snow must close in on them.

Anne snored gently in her own bed. Charlotte rolled over

and sat up, too wide awake for sleep. Heavy-eyed she picked up a French book from the table beside her. She opened it with a great yawn, scarcely able to make out the words in the dull light of early dawn. Suddenly she threw back her covers and pushed out both bare feet to slide them into her shoes. In a moment she had bounced out of bed, out of the room, and down the hall to the room where Branwell slept now, by himself. Without ceremony she flung open his door.

All that was visible of Branwell was a tuft of red hair lying between sheets and pillow, and a slight mound in the middle of a heaving feather bed. Charlotte leaped straight onto the mound and shook it.

"What . . . ?" Branwell, sleepy and furious, opened his eyes at last. "What . . . ?" He turned over. His eyes closed again.

"Wake up! Wake up!" Charlotte shook him. "Branwell, what do you suppose? I have just thought of a new name for the Genii's city of Glasstown!"

"Umph!" Branwell pulled the sheet up closer about his neck. His eyes remained firmly closed.

"I am going to call it Verreopolis!"

"Very . . ." His lips formed the word with a tremendous effort. He gave up the attempt. "Oh, go away, and stop bothering me."

"It's from the French!" Charlotte persisted. Her mouth was at his ear. *"Verre* means *glass* in French, you know. Branwell, wake up and listen to me!"

His sleepy eyes blinked open. He growled:

"Silly Genii! Silly Glasstown! Can't you ever think of anything but that stupid old game? I don't care what you call it. Only let me sleep!"

Charlotte's numb hands fell to her sides. Branwell was right. It was silly to be so excited over a childish play. After all it was not a real novel. The Glasstown play was only a game. She turned and crept away, back to her own bed.

But by breakfast time Branwell was thoroughly awake and in a much better humor. They breakfasted alone. Papa was not at home. He had been away from home nearly a week, now. He was paying his long-delayed visit to Uncle Fennel.

It was rather exciting to breakfast without Papa. They could talk as loud as they wished, and play catch across the table with their spoons when Tabby was not looking.

All morning they played games on the Moor. A gray, thick cold was on the hills, and the wind blew so fiercely that even Emily dared not sit down at all; so they played they were having the African Olympic Games, and raced up and down over winding footpaths.

Charlotte had to set the limits for the races: from Sladen Beck down to the Bottom; from the rocks, which had once formed their great school on Vision Island, to the three lonely farmhouses at the Withens; and back across the bare stretches of hills on a single footpath leading from Ponden Clough.

Four famished Genii made the most of Tabby's dinner. They ate as much as they could hold of potatoes and ham and Tabby's own golden rice pudding. Even Charlotte, who would not touch meat, ate an extra potato loaded down with butter, and two helpings of pudding.

After dinner they went out again, muffled and mittened. Tabby warned them:

"Make the best o' today. 'Twill be th' last upon th' Moor for ye. 'Tis endin' on snow by this even."

They felt the wind through the woolly wraps, as they ran out through the lane and clambered up the bank, on the hard, frozen ground. Blue clouds hung over the hills of withered heather and dead bracken.

With chattering teeth Charlotte ordered:

"Let us run up, once again, to our own hollow by Sladen Beck, to bid it 'good winter.' "

They ran clumsily in their heavy clothes. Once Anne stumbled and nearly fell, her ankle twisting in a root.

"Are you hurt?" Charlotte's voice seemed to echo back upon her as she ran to help Anne up to her feet.

Anne gathered her wits slowly, stamping both feet to make sure they were unhurt.

"No! I think not. It was a stem, I think. Yes! Look, this must be it!" She stopped to pick it up. "See, is it not queer? It is heather . . . like bell heather. But it is not purple; it is pure white!"

"White heather!"

Emily had turned and knelt down suddenly in the place where Anne was looking. In a cleft of the rock, and protected almost miraculously from the fierce wind by the hillside above it, grew a single gallant clump of the frail blossoms. Branwell repeated:

"White heather! Ah, that is luck! Let us wish on it!"

"We'll wish." Charlotte's voice was a whistle in the wind. "We'll wish on it when we get to Sladen Beck, to make our farewell to the Moor."

It took all their strength to make headway against the gale. Around the horizon the gray clouds gathered and mounted, pile on pile. Winter was very close to the black pools and the withered heath, as they came at last to the stone bridge on the ice-crusted beck.

Anne's cheeks were nearly blue with the cold. Their teeth chattered. In the hollow where they had lain so often in summer sunshine they crouched close to each other.

Now there was not a trace of sunshine in the low-banked clouds. The grass was black as the blossomless heather on every side.

"Oh, Charlotte, it is so cold!" chattered Anne. "Let me go home! Oh, do let us go home!"

Charlotte, her own teeth chattering and hitting together at the icy blast of the wind, insisted:

"No . . . not until we have made a wish for farewell. We must wish—all of us, beside our waterfall—all of us—on white heather."

Branwell, whose own nose was purple, stuck his hands deep in the pockets of his long trousers and pulled his neck down into the fold of his warm woolly ulster.

"Let's hurry or we shall all be frozen like Lot's wife."

"Come then, all Chief Genii, and prepare your wishes!"

In obedience to Charlotte's command the four cold and trembling Genii gathered, in the deepening threat of twilight, about their Chief Genius, Talli. In her right hand, she held the sprig of white heather.

"Wish!" she told them. "The spirit of the Genii is in the wind. To gain your desire, wish!"

The word went riding on the wind. Ginger came padding down to them from the blue and smoky shadows of the hills above, growling, as if some unfamiliar creatures stood among them. Emily and Anne stood silent, watching, in the gray light. With shining face Charlotte stretched the wee white blossom high above her head.

Slowly she passed the bit of heather to Branwell.

"Wish!" she told him.

Branwell held it in his hands for a moment. Then with a nod of satisfaction passed it to Anne. And Anne to Emily. No word was spoken. No sound was heard, save the wind through the long grass on the frozen fields. Once more Charlotte held the white heather in the palm of her hand.

Like a mad yell in her ears came the wind. In this very spot she had said a hundred times with a proud lift of her head:

"I shall be educated. I shall be famous!"

But now, with the white heather between her fingers, came the sound of the icy wind. Its drone was like the loud jeering of fate:

"You will never escape from obscurity. Haworth and the Moor . . . obscurity, ignorance." The words seemed to beat against her ears. "Obscurity! Ignorance! Ignorance! Obscurity!"

A twig snapped sharply beneath Anne's heel. Sharply the desire of Charlotte's heart seemed to crack apart and shrivel in a chill of hopelessness.

The wind tore the slip of heather from between her fingers and sent it, like a spark, along the sweep of blackened heather to the monotonous ever-mounting hills, lost to sight.

"Now," Branwell shrilled, "you've gone and lost it. How can we ever wish on it again?"

Charlotte stood silent, empty-handed, looking into the dimming green sunset.

Twilight, starless and heavy, had already begun to cover

the hills. As they started home, lights came twinkling up from the village. The sound of the wind sank momentarily and the hush that followed was like distance among them. Only the distance held the thoughts of all of them, the distance where the white heather had flown, with their wishes. Gradually the sky grew so dark that even their faces were vague, white, and unreal to each other.

Something stung Anne's cheek. She gave a little exclamation: "Oh, it is snow! I felt it!"

Winter had caught up with them at last. And now they went shrieking home, among the pelting flakes. Ginger bumped clumsily into them, growling in delight.

"I say, I wonder if Papa will be caught in it," shouted Branwell.

"He may be home by now," Charlotte called back, pausing in a headlong leap to straddle a point of rock. "He was expecting to be home today. I heard him say to Aunt that he might be here by tea time."

But a wagoner who had been considerably delayed by the storm stopped by for a moment at the kitchen door to tell Tabby:

"Th' parson will na be back till th' morrow morn. He sent word by th' coach."

Branwell chuckled:

"Papa must be discussing matters of doctrine with Uncle Fennel."

"More likely," Charlotte suggested, "it is the political situation."

Against the window of the parlor the children watched the fall of the first snow storm of winter.

Emily half caught her breath with each twisting streak. It would be that way all up the Moor, now. The black places slowly, slowly, were growing white. The doorstep of Robert Heaton's hut must be covered, and the roof and the rocks and the high heath above Ponden Crag must be white and smooth and utterly impassable.

Charlotte, writing in her little brown copy book, stopped suddenly and looked up to the window at the impenetrable whiteness of moving flakes.

Softly she quoted from her *Tales of the Islanders:*

"Now only fairies dwell in the Island of Dream."

Chapter Thirteen

CHARLOTTE'S DREAM

PAPA arrived home next morning at about dinner time.
The first they knew of his arrival was his voice, loudly
demanding:

"Bring me a cup of hot milk at once, Tabby! I have fallen
three times in a snowdrift, walking from the cross-roads." The
four rushed out of the parlor into the hall to greet his home-
coming.

They gathered around him, asking eager questions about
his visit. Was Uncle Fennel well? Was Cross-Stones as pretty
as ever? Had Uncle Fennel thought to ask about them?

Aunt asked:

"Did my uncle's home appear to be in good order?"

Papa answered them all heartily:

"Yes. Yes, Mr. Fennel is doing well. Very well, indeed, I
should say."

Back in the kitchen, the girls watched Papa's milk heating
in a kettle over the embers.

"I should say," Branwell declared, "that Papa had a very
good time indeed, at Cross-Stones. Did you remark what an
air of satisfaction there was about him?"

"And his face beamed," said Charlotte. "It is amazing. But
Uncle Fennel can put anyone at all into a good humor!"

Even after the milk Papa ate an enormous dinner. He ate
and drank, too hungry to bother with conversation. Finally

Aunt sniffed and wiped her nose and looked over at him, asking:

"And how is Mr. Fennel making out with the woman whom I found to do for him? Is she attending properly to his wants?"

"Excellently. Excellently, my dear Miss Branwell. Your judgment was most wise in selecting her." He swallowed another chunk of bread and gulped his tea. "Her cooking was beyond criticism. Indeed, the very night of my arrival there were other guests besides myself. But it seemed to make no trouble at all for the woman."

"Other guests?" Aunt pricked up her ears. "Were they new acquaintances, may I ask? Were they strangers to you?"

"Indeed, no! They were my friends of many years. Mr. Fennel had invited them entirely on my account. And it was delightful, I assure you, Miss Branwell, to renew our old-time friendship."

"It must have been, indeed. And what were the names of your good friends?"

"Their names? Ah, yes, to be sure. Their names were Mr. and Mrs. Thomas Atkinson."

Charlotte gasped. She could feel the eyes of all the others turning upon her.

Aunt was saying coldly:

"Well, I am sure that I hope Mrs. Atkinson has modified some of her opinions since last she called upon us here."

"Mrs. Atkinson," said Papa, "was most pleasant, indeed. And most cordial. She invited Mr. Fennel and myself not only once, but three times, while I was at Cross-Stones, to take our tea with her."

"Tea!"

It was Charlotte's voice; words came tumbling from her.

"Did you walk into the house with the green-painted doors? Did you walk out into the flower garden, behind the hedge row? Did you actually stand by the fountain? Oh, Papa, how I wish that I could have been with you!"

Papa inclined his head toward her. He was still smiling.

"Well, it is strange that you should feel so interested in that house, especially in view of a conversation which I had with Mrs. Atkinson, concerning you. A conversation, I may say, of some importance!"

Charlotte did not feel that she breathed, waiting for him to go on. Branwell kicked her sharply, beneath the table. Across the table Emily and Anne had stopped eating; they were all looking straight at Papa.

Papa continued:

"Mrs. Atkinson told me that Mr. Fennel had brought it to her mind that she had made some sort of promise to you, concerning the matter of your education. Indeed, we discussed that subject, the three of us together."

His glance turned toward Aunt. He said:

"The matter was concluded, I may say, most satisfactorily, by Mrs. Atkinson's agreeing to pay the fees for a year's term for my daughter Charlotte to go to Miss Wooler's school at Roehead."

Branwell made a sudden choking noise. There was the sound of Emily's gasp, and Anne's.

The meaning of Papa's words whirled into Charlotte's consciousness.

School! Miss Wooler's school at Roehead! The house with the big bowed windows, which Uncle Fennel had pointed out to her on the day of their ride. The school of the pleasant-faced woman, and the happy girls walking along the woods road near Kirkstall Abbey.

It could not be real. It must be a dream.

Flakes of falling snow, beyond the window, danced and blurred before her eyes. But Aunt's voice, speaking, broke the dream.

"I cannot see, Mr. Brontë, that you should put yourself under obligation to Mrs. Atkinson. She is a woman who makes light of the Lord's work among the Wesleyans."

"Oh, please, Aunt!" Charlotte found her voice. Her hands were so tightly clasped together that the nails cut into her flesh. "It will not turn me against the Wesleyans, I promise you."

"Well, I have no doubt upon that score. I have not, I trust, labored with you in good works all these years in vain. However . . ."

Now it was Papa himself who interrupted her.

"I believe that we should not hastily reject so fair a gift as Mrs. Atkinson offers. I myself have noted that my daughter's interest in history and the politics of the day is noteworthy; that her mind, in short, seems altogether better than likely for a female, and quite deserving of an education. Moreover," he added, "the removal of one of our number is bound to lessen the expense of maintaining this household."

It was decided, between Aunt and Papa, to hold the matter under consideration. Charlotte could not even plan a play that day, nor write a syllable. She sat with Branwell, on the stairs, trying in vain to catch, through the closed study door, the meaning in Papa's rumbling voice, and in Aunt's short and vigorous responses.

They could not refuse her godmother's offer. They must not! It was the wish she had made so hopelessly on the white heather: the wish to learn what other girls knew; to learn French and history; to be able to go out and write real books, instead of play manuscripts; to have a real publisher, instead of being "published and sold by Captain Tree, and all other booksellers in Glasstown"; to be an educated woman and take her place without fear among the educated women of the world.

Sitting close beside Branwell, listening with held breath for the opening of the study door, Charlotte swore a deep vow to herself. If only she might have this opportunity, she would work day and night to learn what her teachers might give her. She would give every ounce of her energy to achieve the height and breadth of learning which would equip her to go out un-afraid into the higher circles of the educated world.

She and Anne set the table for tea on tip-toe, almost as if they were in church. Anne said in a troubled way:

"But, Charlotte, if you go away what will we do without you? How shall we make out our play of the Genii?"

Branwell, sitting before the window, answered for her:

"We can't. There will be no more Genii. If Charlotte goes to school the Genii are done with."

Anne objected dolefully:

"But I like them."

Emily said:

"The Genii are never gone from the Moor."

Charlotte, watching the faces of Aunt and Papa as they came in to dinner, knew by the grimness of both that a decision had been reached.

Through Papa's long blessing they sat. Charlotte felt her heart squeezing and pumping against her ribs. Her cheeks flamed hot as he reached over to pick up his knife. She could see her own plate, the whole table, spinning before her in an unsteady haze. Papa's next words shattered that haze into a thousand split sparks.

"Well, daughter, it is settled!" His knife pierced the section of mutton set before him. His hand paused. "It is settled that on the first day of January you will leave Haworth to take up your residence at Miss Wooler's school at Roehead."

Papa's knife slid cleanly through the mutton.

That very afternoon Emily and Anne were pressed by Aunt into frantic service, making long pairs of underwear and cutting patterns for two new frocks for Charlotte.

Charlotte herself saw not a bit of the whirl and drift of endless snow past the windows of the girls' room. In the warm glow of the kitchen fire she worked radiantly upon French verbs and geography.

Branwell, moving restlessly about the house, found little part in all the work going forward. Late in the evenings Aunt faded away wearily to bed, Papa was safely locked in his study, and Anne and Emily sat empty-handed, Ginger panting and warm between them, as they made out silent fire-pictures in the embers. Then it was that Branwell and Charlotte whispered together in the far corner of the kitchen.

They planned and talked about the adventure coming so soon and so unexpectedly to Charlotte, the great adventure of going away to school.

"The only trouble," Charlotte confessed to her brother, "the only trouble for me is going to be about our plays. I know that I shall miss them terribly, no matter how nice school will be. I try to tell myself that I shall not, but it is no use."

Branwell answered her:

"Oh, once you are at Roehead you will think only of how

silly you have been to go romping around the kitchen with a pan for a shield and playing about the Duke of Wellington's palace on the dining-room carpet. You will be grown up, at Roehead."

"That is not what I mean. I know that we are not children any longer. And I do not care about all our foolish, childish games. But, oh, Branwell, how I shall miss the fun that you and I have had, making our *Young Men's Magazine,* and our *Tales of the Islanders,* writing them secretly together, just you and I!"

"What about me? What shall I do without you? There'll be no fun for me, writing here by myself. Don't think that it hasn't occurred to me how dull I shall be, all winter, with no one but Emily and Anne."

"I wonder. . . ." Charlotte hesitated. She began again. "Branwell, do you not think that we might go on with our *Young Men's Magazine,* even if we are not together? We could write out our stories and our poems, and we could send them to each other. We could send them in letters. By the post!"

"In letters? By the post? Well, I am sure I don't know why it could not be managed. Why, Charlotte, I do believe that you have struck upon a scheme!"

"To be sure I have. You can make sketches, or poems, and I will write stories. We could even write stories together. You could begin them, and send me your beginnings to complete."

"We could write a novel!" Branwell suggested eagerly. "I will plan it, and you write it. Or we will both write chapters in turn. Oh, this is a splendid scheme, and far more sport than if we could both be in the same place, for we'll never know what each other is doing to the same characters!"

Papa's step sounded in the hall, and the rasping grind of the high cased clock, being wound up for the night.

"It is time for bed!"

Off flew Charlotte with her last problem of going away solved.

Aunt's problems were by no means solved. Darning and the cutting-up of materials went on at a bustling rate in the parsonage, while snow blew and the wind whistled unheeded outside. Aunt did not intend that Mrs. Atkinson should have another opportunity to criticize her god-daughter's wardrobe.

All the next day it snowed and drifted, but the next morning the sky curved, shining with blue distance over the hills.

It seemed as if the wildest imaginings could not make them out as the same hills as those where the Genii had raced over hard black heath. They were covered, white and glittering to blind the eyes of those who looked. Bushes and rocks jutted up sharply, like black dots against the smooth ocean of snow, an ocean that covered all the hollows and heather and deep bog land in one shining swell, mounting up against the spotless blue above.

Just before dinner teamsters broke through, coming from the village, digging out the road from the snowfall. They stopped in the kitchen for a bite of bread and a bowl of strong tea with Tabby.

They gave vivid accounts of how one of the post coaches had strayed, lost in the storm. The passengers were nearly frozen before rescuers arrived. The teamsters said snow had drifted in the hollows on the Moor until some, who ventured out this morning, had come back with the news that you could not tell hollows from pathways, and that when you missed the path in some places, you would sink up to your neck in snow. They told of two men who had started at the beginning of the snow from Stanbury to go over the Moor on horseback, in spite of all warnings about hidden bogs and treacherous falls on the trail to Haworth. No news had yet been heard of them.

Aunt hovered at the door, with a horrified gasp.

"How terrible! Of course you sent out a searching party at once!"

A teamster shook his head.

"Why should a sensible man risk his neck for th' sake of a couple o' bragging fools? Even th' horses had more sense. Poor dumb brutes! They wouldna have moved an inch from th' stables, but they were driven to 't by th' whip."

The men fell to eagerly upon the bowls of hot brimming tea as it came from Tabby's hands, and munched the bread and butter and mutton with intense satisfaction. Reluctantly they went at last to finish their work of clearing the road.

"Well," Charlotte declared, "I must say I am glad that I shall be going to a warmer and more equitable climate in the near future."

"Warmer! Ho! It's not twenty miles away from here!" jeered Branwell.

"It is warmer, all the same. Aunt says it reminds her of her girlhood home in Penzance. And it is not half so barren. Remember Cross-Stones? There were trees and woods, and no dreary, bare hills, such as are in this little moorland village."

"Aye"—Tabby paused in the act of placing a round, pale, lemon-colored mound of butter on a green dish—"aye, and there's na heather neither t' be seen thereabouts. So I've heard tell."

"No heather!" Emily repeated the words.

Charlotte went on talking as if there had been no interruptions.

"I sometimes believe that Aunt is right. The people who live in this hard climate are not able to appreciate the sweet zephyrs of a milder and warmer sphere. Of course, a crude hard people must really enjoy a hard climate!"

Emily rattled the dishes violently, beginning to set the table. Tabby knelt over her rising cake on the bake stone.

"Aye," she grunted to the glowing peat. " 'Tis hard we are. Hard t' drive a bargain. And hard t' hold a grudge. But more hard t' stick fast to a friend, till there's naught o' th' world can sever us!"

Gradually the great snowfall began to melt.

It melted in patches of mud, impassable mud, more dangerous than the snow itself for horses and wayfarers going over Moor trails. Muddy bogs trapped the unwary under foot.

The girls were kept far too busy preparing for Charlotte's wardrobe to find much time to run out on the Moor. Fingers kept stitching and cutting. Tongues kept up a steady accompaniment to the work, as they discussed every possible phase of the new life which was opening before the oldest sister, a life which would take her far away from them and from Haworth.

Once Emily questioned:

"Will you be allowed to go to Cross-Stones, do you suppose, to visit Uncle Fennel?"

"I hope so," Charlotte answered, and added: "I expect that I shall stay sometimes with my godmother. She lives so close to Roehead. And only think what persons of culture I may meet at the home of Mrs. Atkinson!"

"I should think you would rather visit Uncle Fennel. Persons of culture sound to me," said Emily, "as if they must be dull and drab."

Anne declared:

"Among persons of culture I should not dare to speak a word out loud!"

"I shall not speak," Charlotte told them. "I shall listen. And so I shall learn of them how to become an educated lady."

Suddenly Anne put down her work. She pushed back a wisp of yellow curls which had strayed over her ear. Her blue eyes turned toward Charlotte. She said:

"There is one last favor I would like to ask of you, dear Charlotte, before you go away. Only one."

"And what is that?"

"Before you go I should like it so much if you would take some time from your play with Branwell to make out one more tale for us, for Emily and for me."

Charlotte looked up in sudden amazement. She had forgotten all about the younger girls in the great fun of planning the new novel with Branwell. Slowly she laid down her needle and thread.

"Why, of course. I didn't mean . . . I shall begin your tale this very night, Anne. It is a promise. Promise of a Genius!"

But that night she had scarcely taken up her pen when Branwell came in. He told Charlotte in high excitement:

"Papa says that if I show good promise this winter he is

going to have Mr. Robinson of Leeds to teach me to paint. If I am worthy he thinks that he may be able to afford to send me to study at the Royal Academy in London!"

Anne sighed, envious of them both.

"I do not suppose that I shall ever go to school. Papa will never have money to send me. I've no godmother such as yours, Charlotte. And I know that I am not one-half so clever as you, either."

Charlotte answered her, then, laying aside her beloved pen.

"If I have to be a governess for the rest of my life to pay for it, you and Emily shall both have an opportunity to go to school!"

She took the pen into her hand again. Her eyes wandered vaguely to the shelf where her French Voltaire and her geography book were lying. Smiling suddenly, as one to whom a vision was being revealed, she leaned, her nose close against the copy book, and wrote with a flourish:

"Visits in Verreopolis. . . . Vol. 1. . . . Chapter 1. . . ."

Chapter Fourteen

EMILY'S ISLAND

EMILY woke suddenly with the feeling as if something
were strangling her.

Gasping, she choked to consciousness. Her eyes opened on
the black stillness of early morning. Across her stomach she
felt the weight of Charlotte's arm. Charlotte slept. She must
have stretched out in her sleep. The black beat back upon
Emily's eyeballs as her thoughts cleared to a vivid wakefulness.

Today Charlotte was going away to Roehead. Today Branwell and she and Anne would wave good-by to her, good-by
for four months.

Tomorrow night she would be sleeping alone in this big
bed.

Tomorrow morning she and Anne would do their stint of
sewing in Aunt's room as usual. But Charlotte would be
twenty miles away, in a schoolroom at Roehead.

Tomorrow afternoon Branwell would go down to see his
friends in the village. Only she and Anne would walk together
over the Moor.

From the blackness the faint outline of the window began
to stand out. There were no stars. Last night it had been
moonlight. The moon must be hidden somewhere behind
clouds, and the stars there with it.

Twenty miles was a long way for Charlotte to go over
marshes and through woods, on a long winter-rutted muddy

road. And it would be a gray day tomorrow, with snow perhaps. Even now the wind was rising with the portent of a blizzard.

Emily forced herself to lie still, though the weight of Charlotte's arm was almost an agony. She must not stir. Charlotte would surely wake. Suddenly Charlotte rolled away with her back to Emily. Emily closed her eyes and slept.

Bang! Bang!

It seemed still to be the middle of the night when Papa's pistol split their sleep. Up jumped Charlotte. Anne sleepily roused herself, and demanded to know the time, and if it was not too early for Papa's signal.

"Silly!" Charlotte's voice was husky from sleep. "It's the day I go to Roehead. Don't you remember? Papa said he would let off the pistol at half-past four, so you could all have breakfast with me. And say good-by properly."

Charlotte was already a dim figure pulling on her long clean white underwear which had been laid out carefully on the chair the night before. The pantalets. The fine new lace-edged petticoat. And finest of all, the black silk dress which had taken Aunt a whole week to make, with the help of Charlotte and Anne and Emily.

Charlotte smoothed out the silk folds, almost reverently. She patted the collar straight and tied the long silk sash in a wide bow at her back. Then she ran out and down the hall to knock at the door of Aunt's room. Aunt would want to be sure that she was dressed exactly right to go to Roehead.

Emily and Anne dressed more slowly. Emily threw back the covers of the big bed to let it air, and set the brushes and combs straight on the dresser.

Then she and Anne slid down to the door of Aunt's room to watch the process of Aunt putting up Charlotte's hair. She was fixing it exactly as if Charlotte were a real young lady. The curls were unwound from the curling rags and the frizzes combed out and drawn straight and tight back from her forehead by Aunt's firm hand. When at last she twisted it into a knot like an oblong turnip at the back of Charlotte's neck, there was not the sign of a long curl to be seen.

Charlotte ran to get the bonnet from her closet. It was still in the box, just as it had come last week from Leeds. It had been the most terrific extravagance of all, a real bonnet bought at a real shop!

Breathlessly Emily and Anne watched as Aunt placed it on Charlotte's head. She tied the bow beneath her chin, allowing the lace lappets to fly loose. It was almost solemn in the flickering candle light.

"Now," Aunt told her, "you may go down to breakfast. You will have it in the dining room. Mr. Brontë has already breakfasted."

Branwell joined them as they clattered down the stairs. They stopped for a moment in the kitchen. Emily wished they could have eaten there by the warm glow of the fire, instead of in the dimly lighted dining room. But Aunt had arranged it the night before, in honor of Charlotte.

Tabby brought in porridge and milk, and a special treat of scones and preserves with butter, and placed them on the table with a warning to Charlotte.

"Tha'd best eat thy fill. 'Tis a cold weary way afore thee."

Tabby clumped back to the kitchen.

Branwell gave a disgusted look at his porridge. As he sat

with his elbows hunched over the table, he pulled and twisted the thin ends of his hair into a red, rat's nest.

Directly across from him, prim and stiff as the chair upon which she sat, Charlotte talked nervously, volubly, or lapsed into sudden silences, fumbling at her dress and the strings of her bonnet.

"Just think, Branwell. I shall learn counting, just as you have, and geography and history. Perhaps I shall study from *Arithmetic in Whole and Broken Numbers.*"

Branwell made a grimace.

"Hope you like it!"

"Oh, I don't suppose I shall. But you must learn a good many things you don't like, if you are to become educated. Aunt says so."

They went on for a moment pretending to eat the porridge. The silence was so deep that they could hear Aunt's cough upstairs and Papa moving about in his study.

Charlotte jerked up her head again, and went on talking.

"I wonder if I have forgotten anything."

Heedless of Tabby's warning she had not touched a morsel of porridge or jelly.

Five o'clock struck.

The chimes died to silence again, and ticking kept even pace with Charlotte's tongue. Ticking, ticking, every second closer to the time when the covered cart would come from the Black Bull, John Brown on the driver's seat; the time when she would clamber in beside Papa, and John Brown would call an order to the big black horse and flick the reins; the time when she would drive away into the shadows.

Emily busily covered a scone with butter and jelly, then

just as busily she scraped it off again, in a sticky mass. Anne suddenly let her spoon fall into the porridge.

"The very first minute I find"—Charlotte included them all in a quick glance, her cheeks flushed and pink—"I promise I shall write you a good long letter to tell you about everything. Every single thing I do. What we eat, and how we sleep. I shall send you a plan of our daily routine so you will know what I do every minute of the day. I may even do some sketches of the countryside. . . ."

Branwell roused himself long enough to put in a question.

"I say, you'll not let on, will you, about Verreopolis and our play and all that?"

Charlotte answered with a sudden slight lift of her chin.

"You may rest assured that I shall consider it a closed subject. No one at Roehead shall ever know about our play. That is only for us to know!"

The force of her words seemed to accent the light of the two candles and two leaping shadows against the wall. Charlotte's face was a dull gray in the oval of her black bonnet as she added huskily, her eyes glittering, focused on the flame:

"Secret of the Genii!"

Branwell rallied to the old name. He swung around toward Charlotte in eager agreement.

"Neither shall I tell of our play. Not though all the drawing teachers in Leeds should be pining to know."

Emily laid her jellied cake down on her plate and shoved it away from her.

"I guess," Branwell offered, "they won't allow you to leave Roehead. You'll probably have to stay there and study all the time."

"No, indeed," Charlotte countered. "The young ladies take walks, long walks, all over the countryside. Don't you remember seeing them that time we went for a ride at Uncle Fennel's?"

"Twenty miles," Anne murmured. "It isn't so very far away, is it, Charlotte? Roehead, I mean, from here?"

"Of course not. And the post comes very often from Haworth. I shall write you with every post."

"If you don't," Branwell threatened, "I shall go to Roehead myself to find out the reason. Even if I must walk all the way and back again."

Aunt came bustling in with a pair of her own best silk gloves clasped in her hands.

"I could not sleep last night," she told Charlotte, "turning over in my mind what gloves you should wear on Sabbaths. The gray silk will not by any means be proper, and your hands have completely outgrown your own black. No doubt it is because of the swelling effect of so much of this treacherous Moor wind. But that is beside the point. Now take these and place them in your box at once. I will not have you a disgrace to Haworth parsonage when you attend the services in the church at Hartshead."

"But, Aunt," Charlotte protested, "that is your best pair of gloves. What will you wear on Sabbaths here? I'll not take them!"

"Charlotte, do not attempt an impertinence on your last day at home. Do as I command you, regarding the gloves!"

Charlotte opened her box, which lay conspicuously in the middle of the floor. It was the box which she and Emily had brought with them five years ago when they came home with

Papa from Cowan Bridge School. It had been among the luggage which Aunt had taken with them on their visit to Uncle Fennel.

It had been a masterpiece of Aunt's ingenuity to pack, this time. She had used every available space. Carefully she had folded in layer after layer of underclothes and dresses, carefully wrapped the shoes in bagging. Even Charlotte's Bible and her Thomas à Kempis's *Imitation of Christ* went into the big box under Aunt's supervising eyes.

Aunt did not see all that went into that box. She did not see five new thin little copy books, blank except for one or two close-written pages.

It was only Branwell and Emily and Anne who knew about those little books. It was only Branwell who knew what had been written in them already, and on what subjects the remainder would be written.

Charlotte managed to find a place for the gloves. She packed them in smoothly so that they should not muss, and closed the strap once more upon the box.

Tabby came striding in from the kitchen to gather the dishes. "Dost na liken th' porridge?" She stood bleakly over Charlotte. "Dost say 'tis burnt? Tha'st na touched so much as a spoonful."

"Oh, Tabby, I couldn't. I could not eat the finest porridge in the world this morning. It would choke me!"

Tabby, by no means disposed to return to the kitchen, glared down upon Charlotte's finery. Charlotte pushed back her chair, stood up slowly, smoothing out the folds of her new silken gown and pulling her bonnet string straight beneath her big round chin.

"Humph! So tha'rt th' fine lady already." Tabby glowered. "Giving thyself airs!"

Charlotte turned about suddenly and, to her own intense dismay, felt that her chin was trembling, that her eyes felt foggy and damp.

In another moment, she had thrown herself, finery and all, upon Tabby, her arms encircling the great waist in almost a grip of panic.

"Oh, Tabby, don't. Do not say that, please! I shall never be a lady, if being a lady will make me too fine for all of you. Truly, truly, I shall never be so fine that I do not love you best."

"Na." Tabby's voice was thick and heavy as Ginger's growl. "Na, I'm sure tha will na. Tha'st been raised too nigh th' earth o' th' Moor, e'er t' get th' smell out o' tha nose."

The clatter and stamping of the horse's hoofs without announced at last the arrival of John Brown. They were to travel to Roehead in the covered cart.

Papa emerged from the study bundled heavily, with earpads below his round fur cap and a woolen comforter hiding the silk cravat about his neck. His hands were black-mittened.

Charlotte wore a heavy black cape which had once belonged to Emily. It was wool-lined, proof against the raw bleakness of the morning air.

As Papa threw open the door, Aunt peered into the gray morning, shivered, and said:

"No, it will not be enough. Emily! Hasten. Fetch me two of the blankets from Mr. Brontë's room."

Emily ran upstairs, two steps at a time, and was down before Tabby and John Brown had managed to stow away the carpetbag in the recesses of the cart.

At the foot of the stairs, she encountered Branwell, nearly

colliding with him in the dimness. As he rushed past her, he shouted:

"I'm going too, part of the way to Halifax. Papa says I may, if I will walk home."

It was as much as Charlotte could do to climb up to the high seat. Her short legs could not possibly reach to the hub of the great wheel, until Tabby gave her a push from behind and Papa pulled from above. Then up she went over the wheel. Next came the blankets, to be wrapped warmly about her feet.

Aunt stood back, her teeth chattering, in the shelter of the doorway.

"Do not forget!" she called out. "Do not forget to change your good dress immediately upon your arrival at Roehead."

The wind seemed to blow the words from her lips.

Branwell came dashing out of the house and clambered up into the back of the cart. John Brown cracked the whip across the back of the big horse, and they started off.

"Good-by! Good-by!" Charlotte's mittened hand waved to them, as long as they were in sight, until the dimness of distance swallowed up the cart and the plodding horse. Papa, tall on the box, with Charlotte's slight black figure beside him, John Brown, burly and huge, and Branwell curled in the back.

The sky was just beginning to brighten to a grayness. Emily and Anne stood watching as the cart lumbered down the curving road, past the church, past the Black Bull Inn.

Aunt turned and went into the house, blowing her nose violently on her big handkerchief. Emily noticed, looking up suddenly at her, that there were tears in her eyes, more than could be accounted for by the coldness of the wind, that her nose was red.

Tabby clumped away.

Upstairs Aunt's door slammed with a highly unlady-like noise.

"I think"—Anne shivered—"I'll go in with Tabby. It is so cold out here."

Emily stood looking down the empty road long after Anne and Aunt and Tabby had gone in. It was morning light by now, but still gray and terribly ugly and patchy across the Moor. The bogs were full of dirty snow.

She opened the door, calling to Ginger. The house rang emptily to her call. Ginger came padding around the corner, from the direction of the out-kitchen.

A moment more and she was running up the little lane, away from the emptiness of the house to the full sound of the wind, with Ginger at her heels, to somewhere, anywhere, on the Moor. Anywhere to escape the echoing in her ears of the creak of cart wheels long-vanished down the road to Keighley.

Perhaps it was that echo. Perhaps it was the wind guiding her steps. Emily knew only that she was going toward Ponden Crag.

It was not that she had intended going there. Nor had she intended to stop, as she did, by Sladen Beck, to watch the slow water lapping against its banks between tall rushes, hardly disturbing the black still pools among the rocks.

She stood at the edge of the hollow which had once been the scene of the adventures of the Islanders. Her feet stood on the rock where the Twelve Adventurers had once met ship-wreck. Her eyes traveled along trails where they had raced a hundred times in their African Olympic Games. Black rocks and snow-filled hollows marked out the scenes of other games. Hardly a place, as far as she could see from Sladen Beck, had not been marked out for the plays of the Genii.

The black bare heath spread nakedly, lifelessly. But spring would follow winter. Spring would touch the heath magically to life.

But when Spring would arrive this year the four Chief Genii would not appear to reclaim their country. Chief Genius Talli was gone. Chief Genius Branni would go, before another summer, to Leeds. The play of the Genii was over and done with forever. The Country of the Genii had no inhabitant left to claim it for his own.

Emily turned away, the blackness of the winter bogs before her eyes. By instinct her feet took the trail which led to Ponden Crag.

She clambered, with Ginger behind her, over the three stone walls which surrounded the deserted farmhouses at the Withens. On she went, past Ponden House, splashing through thin ice over the stream in Ponden Clough, climbing the last steep ascent to Ponden Crag.

Here was the end of the trail. Here Emily sat down, with Ginger at her feet, her back to the stone wall of the crag.

Morning did not lift the clouds or lessen the bitter choking force of the wind, as time went darkly on. In the ugly Moor below snow-patches served only to bring out the dirtiness of the heath and the withered grass upon it. The wind shrieked ever monotonously the same under its deepening tone, greater intensity. Not even the roundness of a cloud relieved the thick gray oval of the sky. For the first time in her life she felt the chill of the empty Moor.

Suddenly Ginger raised his head. Emily's body went rigid. In the ugliness of the Moor, in the darkness of the empty gray sky and the high heath, almost like the quiver of black heather beneath her feet, Emily felt something clear and new creep upon her thought. Like a crash beyond the hearing of ears, like an unseen flash of lightning, something moved clearly, distinctly, in her senses; something of the snow, and the ugliness, and the loud wind; the rock jutting roughly above out of the emptiness, out of the monotony. Forms began to sharpen to life.

For the first time, for Emily, the real inhabitants of the high heath were making their presence known to her. For the first time she began to look at them, to see them as her own creation.

There was the sudden gleam of black armies, marching on the Moor. Arms clattering against the high rocks. A face flashing white beneath the gleam of black hair and a snow-heavy sky. The single figure of a man striding alone across the heather, his head high-lifted to the rocks above. A woman coming, her face paler than snow, her eyes like the green light before a storm.

There were more wild new faces: faces that had never been seen by Charlotte in her plays, creatures unknown to the Kingdom of the Genii. Here were stern, hard-faced men and women with the unrelenting hardness of the Moor in them, and the Moor's ugliness. And the beauty of the Moor was in them, too.

They were the people of Emily's kingdom. Their suffering and bravery and loneliness were hers. And Emily claimed them for her own.

Slowly her lips formed words. In her throat came a sound like the growl of the wind.

"They are the Gondals."

From every side they were coming to her. Their advance was faster than the march of feet, their faces nearer to her than the reach of her hands, too near to see. She knew that their eyes were clear, their heads lifted toward the tops of the hills, like all the folk who dare to challenge life on the Moor. And she knew that a boy stood nearest of them all, a dark-haired lad, with no smile on his mouth.

Suddenly she felt that his eyes smiled, looking toward her, as a lad's eyes had once, long before, in the soft glow of a peat fire, in the shadows of a wee gray hut on the edge of a shaking Moor.

Again she spoke aloud to name him:

"Heathcliffe!"

She did not even feel that her cheeks were colorless with cold, or that sensation had gone from her feet. Ginger slid down from beside the walled rock and slunk, shivering, down along the clough and back toward home. But Emily sat on, immovable, with the black people of her creation about her.

Snow began, in thin flakes, to fall against her cheek. Her lips were moving again and, in her thoughts, beginning to make words.

From the rocks and the hills and the terrible gray sky and the ugliness below, phrases and sentences and words came to her:

High waving heather, 'neath stormy blasts bending,
Midnight and moonlight and bright shining stars,
Darkness and glory rejoicingly blending,
Earth rising to heaven and heaven descending,
Man's spirit away from the drear dungeon sending,
Bursting the fetters and breaking the bars.

All down the mountainsides wild forests lending
One mighty voice to the life-giving wind,
Rivers their banks in the jubilee rending,
Fast through the valleys a reckless course wending,
Wilder and deeper their waters extending,
Leaving a desolate desert behind.

Shining and lowering and swelling and dying,
Changing forever from midnight to noon,
Roaring like thunder, like soft music sighing,
Shadows on shadows advancing and flying,
Lightning-bright flashes the deep gloom defying,
Coming as swiftly and fading as soon.

At last, more gently, came to her:

> There should be no despair for you
>   While nightly stars are burning,
> While evening pours its silent dew
>   And sunshine gilds the morning;
> There should be no despair, though tears
>   May flow down like a river;
> Are not the best beloved of years
>   Around your heart forever?

Emily stood up at last, stiff from cold. She turned away
from Ponden Crag without a backward look, treading over
the snow-covered rocks and going swiftly down the Moor.

Time must have passed. Dinner would be ready. Anne would be looking for her to come home.

Snow fell faster with the stir of the wind. Emily ran on in long strides. Her dark hair spread back upon the moaning wind, snow whirled about her upturned face. Her legs moved to the rhythm of the echoing words in her thought:

> There should be no despair, though tears
> May flow down like a river;
> Are not the best beloved of years
> Around your heart forever?

AN AFTERWORD

THIS tale, as I have told it, has been of the childhood and growing-up days of the four Brontë geniuses, or Genii, as they would rather have been remembered. It is an attempt to delve back through the few incidents known of them then into the years when they were free upon the Moor, and undivided.

I have tried to show the Moor and Haworth not as an impediment to their genius, as Charlotte Brontë and her biographer Mrs. Gaskell believed, but as the holy place of its conception. It is surely true that in Haworth the four young Brontës began to weave their web of words and the "making out" of the characters and tales which foreshadowed their poetry and finally the creation of *Jane Eyre* and *Wuthering Heights*.

As far as possible I have tried to follow strictly the chronological order of events as they took place in the lives of this remarkable family, during the years 1825 to 1830. The other characters introduced in this book really lived also.

And the magic of the Genii is always real.

BIBLIOGRAPHY

E. F. Benson, *Charlotte Brontë* (New York, 1932)

Augustine Birrell, *Life of Charlotte Brontë* (London, 1887)

Mrs. Ellis H. Chadwick, *In the Footsteps of the Brontës* (London, 1914)

Joseph Craven, *A Brontë Moorland Village and Its People: A History of Stanbury* (Keighley, 1907)

Mrs. Elizabeth C. Gaskell, *Life of Charlotte Brontë, with an Introduction by Clement Shorter* (London, 1900)

G. R. Gleig, *Life of Arthur, Duke of Wellington* (Everyman's Library)

A. Jessop, *Penny History of the Church of England* (London, 1911)

Francis Leyland, *The Brontës, with Special Reference to Patrick Branwell Brontë* (London, 1886)

Fannie E. Ratchford, *Legends of Angria* (New Haven, 1933)

Mary F. Robinson, *Emily Brontë* (London, 1883)

Clement Shorter, *Charlotte Brontë and Her Circle* (London, 1896)

Clement Shorter, *Life and Letters of Charlotte Brontë* (New York, 1908)

Elizabeth Southwart, *Brontë Moors and Villages—from Thornton to Haworth* (New York, 1923)

Robert Southey, *Life of Wesley,* Volume II (New York, 1847)

Romer Wilson, *Emily Brontë* (New York, 1928)

T. J. Wise and J. A. Symington, *The Shakespeare Head Brontë* (Oxford, 1934)